Prejudice and Pardon

ISBN: 978-1-947319-77-6

Cover and text layout design: Kristi Yoder

Printed in the USA

Published by:

TGS International
P.O. Box 355
Berlin, Ohio 44610 USA
Phone: 330.893.4828
Fax: 330.893.2305
www.tgsinternational.com

TGS001741

Prejudice *and* Pardon

In the face of injustice, Lillie finds grace to forgive

Laura Smucker

Table of Contents

Preface

I first met Sister Lillie in 2011. "Someone should write her story," I remarked to her church family. Four years later, I was surprised to be asked to interview Sister Lillie and write her story. By that time, she was ninety years old and suffering from congestive heart failure. It was important to go as quickly as I could. So I made plans to travel from Oregon to Pennsylvania and spend part of a week with her.

Although Sister Lillie knew she would soon pass over Jordan, her testimony of God's grace was evident by the radiant joy on her face. It was all because of Him that she survived the many hardships she faced as a black person in a prejudiced nation. "You all are thin-skinned," she told me. "You don't really know what a hard life is like." And she is right. I have done my best to relay her story to you in the same spirit she told it to me. Many details have been added to make the story flow, and I have consolidated some characters to avoid confusion.

"I have been on a quest for God," she told me, "and He has placed me among the Mennonites to finish my course. From there He will pass me over to my Father in heaven to be the bride of Christ." These were some of her last words to me. As I was preparing to leave the next morning for my flight home, she phoned me. "I have another word from the Lord for you to share with those who read my story," she said. I assured her I would pass the verses on to you, my readers:

> *For other foundation can no man lay than that is laid, which is Jesus Christ* (1 Corinthians 3:11).

> *And this is life eternal, that they might know thee the only true God, and Jesus Christ, whom thou hast sent* (John 17:3).

Lillie's life glows with love for Jesus Christ. As you read her story, may your love for Him increase.

chapter one

Miracle in the Cotton Field

"Mammaw, why can't I have beautiful dresses like Sue's?" Six-year-old Lillie Johnson's black eyes cast a longing glance toward the big plantation house on the hill. Then she looked up into her grandmother's wrinkled face.

Mammaw shook her finger at Lillie. "When will you just 'cept the fact that you be poor, chile? You are beautiful. No reason to be 'shamed of the clothes God gave you. You look pretty in any ol' rags! Hallelujah! Praise de Lawd!"

Lillie sighed. *I'll never be beautiful,* she thought. The sun peppered her nose with freckles in spite of her dark skin. She walked outside and sat on the rickety front porch steps, propping her chin in her hands. Sue's house had pretty flowered wallpaper and a doll house and books and only three people in it besides the servants. In 1931, the gap between black and white living conditions stretched as wide as the Mississippi River.

Lillie lived in Canton, Mississippi, in a chinked-log shack with her grandparents whom she called Pappaw and Mammaw, her Mama Belle and Daddy James, her brothers Tucker and Walker, and Aunt Bernice and Uncle George. Each family had a room for sleeping, and they shared the fourth room for cooking and living. Pappaw and Mammaw took the lead in their home.

"Thank ya, Jesus," Pappaw would say. "We have us four good rooms to live in. God is so good to us." Pappaw often talked about God and prayed to Him. He reminded the children not to lie or cheat or steal. Pappaw insisted they thank God for the things He provided. Lillie never understood why she should be thankful for their tumbledown house. She wished they had one with beautiful walls like the house on the hill. The house where Sue lived, with her beautiful dresses.

"Lillie," Mama Belle called the next morning, "let's get up and movin'. The sun will be shinin' on us in an hour, and it'll be hot before we know it."

Lillie opened her eyes in the windowless bedroom with its newspaper-plastered walls. Light shone through the cracks. In the winter, the winds whistled and blew through the cracks, but today it was summer—cotton-picking season. Mama Belle, Daddy James, Tucker, and Walker had already gotten up. Their beds stood empty, their faded coverlets smoothed.

The cornhusks inside the mattress rustled as Lillie swung her feet over the edge of her pallet bed. She smoothed the lumpy cotton coverlet and plumped the feather pillow. She lifted her flour sack dress off its hook. "Ugly dress," she muttered to herself. *Mmm, I smell Mammaw's fresh biscuits.* Lillie hurried to the kitchen. She spread molasses on her hot biscuit and stuffed her mouth full.

The morning sun was already beating down as one by one the family stepped out of the shack. No one was excused from the hard task awaiting them. Even six-year-olds like Lillie were expected to work as hard and as long as their elders did. They slung their cotton sacks over their shoulders. Their dusty feet made footprints in the dirt. Lillie's small bare feet followed Pappaw's. She tried to take big steps like he did, but her feet soon hurt from the rocks that poked through the dirt.

"Let's sing," Mammaw said.

Pappaw led out:

> To the River of Jordan our Savior went one day
> And we read that John da Baptist met him there.
> And when John baptized Jesus in Jordan's rushin' waters
> The mighty power of God filled de air.

The whole family joined in:

> I'm on my way to da River of Jordan
> Gonna wade right in to da rushin' waters
> I'm going down to da River of Jordan
> And let da cool waters cleanse my soul.[1]

Lillie forgot about her aching feet as she sang. The cotton field, studded with plants bearing snowy balls of fiber, lay close to their house. Mister Big Ike planted the fields as close as possible to the edge of the Johnsons' plot, just as he did with all his sharecroppers. He didn't want to waste any space that could be used for cash crops.

Mister Ike expected his workers to sing as they worked. In years past, a silent slave met disapproval from his owners. Slave owners wanted their slaves to sing because it lifted their morale.

Pappaw began singing an old work song from slavery days, and soon everyone was chanting as they worked:

> Tamp 'em up solid all the livelong day.
> Tamp 'em up solid, den they'll hold that midnight mail.
> The captain don't like me. Won't allow me no show.
> Well, work don't hurt me, don't care where in da world I go.[2]

The whole family picked from dawn until dark as the cotton continued to ripen. Their backs ached from bending over. Their hands grew rough and sore from picking. The cotton bolls had hard, sharp petals encircling the fluff. But Lillie never heard Pappaw complain. Growing up as a slave, then becoming a sharecropper on the same plantation, Pappaw knew no other life. Pappaw's parents had hoped that the plantation would be divided among the newly freed slaves so they could provide for themselves. Instead, the plantations seized during the Civil War were returned to their former owners, and the farms were parceled out to sharecroppers. Even though slavery had officially ended, their lives as sharecroppers formed another kind of slavery through the unfair treatment from their landlords.

Someday I want a different life than Pappaw had, Lillie thought. She slung the strap of her dirty cotton sack over her thin shoulder. Dragging the sack along, she stooped to pull the white fluff from the rows and rows of bushes. Using both hands, she stripped each stalk clean, carefully trying to avoid the sharp burrs at the bottom of the bolls.

"Ouch!" she yelled as a burr caught her finger. She popped the stinging finger into her mouth to stop the bleeding. She blinked back the tears and reached for the next cotton plant.

The summer rains had kept the cotton loose and fluffy, so the bolls readily yielded the little clouds of cotton. Most years the bolls grew small and tight; then the pickers had to harvest the entire boll, sharp petals and all, and allow the cotton gin to do the separating.

The loose cotton began to collect in Lillie's sack. She worked contentedly next to Tucker, her older brother. "Whew," he said, his face glistening with sweat, "it's so hot this mornin', I see monkeys dancin'." Her family's way of describing the heat always brought a giggle from Lillie.

"Just wait till afternoon." Lillie wiped her forehead with the back of her hand. Hundred-degree fall days didn't stop the pickers. They knew their lives depended on what they could pick during daylight hours. "Pappaw," Lillie asked when she got to the end of her row, "will we finish this field tonight?"

Pappaw wiped his arm over his dusky brow. He gazed at row after row of cotton waiting to be picked. "Lawd willin', we will," he said. "An' it's a good crop too. I hope we get at least seventeen bales like last year."

At two thousand pounds a bale, seventeen bales was a lot of cotton. Of course, even an abundance of cotton didn't guarantee a good wage for the sharecropper. That all depended on Mister Big Ike, who set the wage with his own profits in mind. He would make sure he got his share of the crops. This year half of their earnings had to go for the seed and tools Pappaw had purchased on credit for spring planting. He might get only seven hundred dollars for a whole year of work, but he would accept it. His brother Eddy had been thrown off the plantation last year because he had tried to figure out if he had gotten his fair share. Pappaw wouldn't risk it. He had to accept what Mister Big Ike gave them, or the whole family would starve.

Lillie's bag bulged with cotton, but she didn't want to go alone to the edge of the field to get it weighed. Sometimes Mister Big Ike showed up unannounced. His narrow eyes watched the cotton pickers while he puffed on his big cigar. Lillie's insides trembled just thinking about it. No way did she want to face Mister Big Ike by herself. *I'll just wait for Tucker,* she thought. *His sack is almost full.*

Lillie watched her younger brother Walker trudge toward the house for water. He slid the slatted wooden cover off the well in the yard and turned the crank to lower the bucket. The thought of the bucket sloshing with fresh water made Lillie's throat feel parched. Walker picked up the bucket and brought it back to his family. When it was her turn at the dipper, Lillie drank as slowly as possible and reluctantly passed the dipper to Tucker. The short break gave them energy to keep picking.

Soon Tucker had filled his sack. "Want me ta walk with you ta the wagon?" he asked.

Lillie sighed with relief. She nodded as she yanked on her sack to drag it to the waiting wagon. Tucker followed her carrying his bag, which weighed even more.

When they neared the wagon, the man in charge of weighing cotton jumped down to help them. "Looks like some full sacks here," he said,

Cotton scales

tying Lillie's sack to the bottom of the scale that hung from a nearby tree limb. "Let's see." He slid the weight down the metal ruler until it balanced perfectly. "Good job, Lillie," he said as he noted the weight of her lumpy sack. He hefted the sack over the edge of the wagon, dumped the fluff onto the growing pile of cotton, then handed the empty sack back to Lillie.

Next he weighed and emptied Tucker's sack. "Now the wagon's full," he said, handing the sack back to Tucker. He untied the horses from the nearby shade tree and hitched them to the wagon. Climbing into the wagon, he grabbed the reins. "Giddyap!" he shouted, slapping the reins against the horses' rumps. The full wagon creaked and groaned as it turned down the road.

"Where's he takin' all that cotton?" Lillie asked.

"To Canton," Tucker answered. "They'll bale it and haul the bales to the cotton gin in the next town."

"What's a cotton gin?" Lillie asked.

"I've never seen one," Tucker said. "Pappaw seen one once. Ask him. Come now, we gotta fill our sacks again."

Lillie reluctantly turned back to the field. Her bag wouldn't be full again all day. She reached down to pull the cotton off the next waiting bush.

"Watch out!" Tucker shouted. "A snake!"

Lillie jerked her hand back in terror. But she was too late. The poisonous fangs of the hidden copperhead had struck Lillie's hand. "Pappaw, Pappaw!" she cried. "I'm gonna die."

Pappaw dropped his bag and lunged down the row toward his

granddaughter. He grabbed Lillie's hand and looked at it closely. Redness spread over her hand. "Mm-mm. That's quite a bite." Calmly he laid his hand on it and raised his head to the heavens. "Almighty God, you promised ta answer our meager prayers if we come ta you in faith."

By this time the others had gathered around. "I ask ya, Lawd, in the name of Jesus, ta take the venom out of Lillie's hand. I know you have the power ta heal her," Pappaw continued.

No one said "Amen!" to Pappaw's prayer. Lillie wished her Daddy James had faith like Pappaw. Pappaw prayed in simple, humble faith. Praying was a way of life for him, and this was another problem he took to his Lord. Prayer was their survival. They had no money for doctors or hospitals.

Again Pappaw looked closely at Lillie's hand. "Thank ya, Lawd," he prayed, tears running down his cheeks. "You're so faithful."

Lillie looked down through her own tears and saw the redness was disappearing. She sniffled and rubbed her eyes. Pappaw drew her close and hugged her tightly. If she ever found Pappaw's God, Lillie would know she had found the real thing. Looking up into Pappaw's kind brown face, she thought, *Someday I'll be just like him.*

That evening while Mammaw made supper and Mama Belle scrubbed the floor with lye to keep it white, Lillie asked Pappaw, "What's a cotton gin?"

Pappaw sat back in the creaky rocker and explained, "It's a wonderful big machine that saves us lots of work. It separates the cotton from the seeds that are stubborn hangin' on. Without it, cleanin' cotton is well-nigh impossible."

Lillie awoke the next morning to the drumming of rain on the roof. Picking cotton would be out of the question today. Maybe she could go fishing with Daddy James. Lillie bounded out of bed and hurried to pull on her dress and tie back her kinky hair with a ribbon.

Sliding into a bench at the table, Lillie waited while Pappaw led the whole family in a prayer. "Oh, Lawd, we praise ya for the rain today. You know our sore hands need a rest now and then. Praise de Lawd! And for our food, thank ya, Jesus! Amen."

Lillie quickly ate her biscuit spread with butter and molasses. She glanced at Daddy James seated across the table.

He winked at her. "Wanna go fishin' today? It might be your last chance before school."

Lillie nodded, her mouth too full to speak.

"Bring home a whole mess of 'em, James," Mama Belle said. "We can have fresh fried fish this evening."

Lillie followed her father through the pasture to the creek. She sat on the bank as Daddy James checked the fishing seine for holes. He tied rocks along the bottom of the net so it sank to the bottom where the fish couldn't swim under it. He tied his precious cork pieces along the top so the edge would float, making a better trap for the fish. Lillie felt close to Daddy James as they worked together to prepare the nets for fishing. He wasn't full of faith like Pappaw, but he was kind.

Lillie grabbed one side of the net and held on while Daddy James walked across the murky creek carrying the other side. "Let's go," he said as he trolled the net through the water.

"Ready!" Lillie called, and she heaved the net with all her might. Then they lifted it from the water to see bass, creel, minnows, and lampreys leaping and wiggling.

"Don't want these lampreys." Daddy James lifted the eel-like creatures and dropped them back into the water. The locals considered them poisonous, even though they were actually edible. Lillie hated when they attached their sucking mouths to her feet under the water and she had to peel them off her skin. They didn't like to let go and always left a red welt.

Soon their sack bulged with fish. Lillie walked home beside her father. She always felt like "Daddy James's girl" when they were fishing together. "Think Mama Belle will make corn pone ta go with our fresh fish?" Lillie asked.

He reached down and took her hand. "Sure hope so. It'll be a feast for all of us."

When they got home, Daddy James helped Mama Belle clean the fish. Then Mama Belle dipped each slab into cornmeal and laid it in a frying pan bubbling with bacon fat. It sizzled as it fried to a delicious brown. The family gathered, each holding a tin plate, waiting for a fresh piece of fish. Belle pulled the corn pone out of the coals and piled some on each plate along with a generous helping of bass. "Mmmm!" Lillie's mouth was too full to say more. She ate a second piece and then a third. She was sure nothing in the world tasted as good as freshly caught fish.

The cotton picking lasted three months. Next came the peanut harvest, then the corn and sugarcane. Each day dragged by on leaden feet, filled with hours of exhausting labor. Every year after crops were in, Pappaw hoped to pay down the debt he had accumulated farming with Mister Big Ike, but every year the debt seemed to grow. Always borrowing to prepare for harvest and almost never being able to pay back bound the blacks to their plantation owner and their crops. The unfairness of the system made some people bitter, but not Pappaw. People considered him "high-class," one who made something of himself and earned the respect of others. His life demonstrated integrity and the fullness of God's Spirit.

chapter two

A Day of Rest

Mammaw pulled a rag from her bosom and passed it around until all the members of the family had wiped their shoes shiny clean. After walking the three miles to church, their shoes were covered with road dust. A hand-painted sign in front of the simple, clapboard structure read "Hopewell Methodist Church."

Pappaw strode up the aisle to the front of the church and turned to face his neighbors and fellow sharecroppers. He lifted his hand in blessing. "Most holy and mighty God, here we are again, standing before ya. We came to say thank ya. You've been so good."

"Yes, Lawd!" the congregation responded.

Lillie hurried to a side room to find her choir robe. She could hear Pappaw's deep voice as he continued praying.

"And Jesus," Pappaw continued as he raised his face and hands heavenward, "you gave us another chance to praise ya."

"Yes, Lawd!"

"As you remember us, we ask ya to make our problems light."

"Have mercy, Lawd," the congregation chanted. People were beginning to warm up now.

Pappaw dropped on his knees, eyes still heavenward. "Lawd, we know you care 'bout us. The pain, the anguish of our souls. We pray ya stay with us to the end. Amen!" Pappaw bent his head to the floor.

"Amen!"

By now Lillie and the rest of the choir members had donned their robes and filed to the front. Lillie stood in the front row between two friends. Their white robes swayed as they chanted in song.

> There is a balm in Gilead to make the wounded whole;
> There is a balm in Gilead to heal the sin-sick soul.[1]

The congregation stood, swaying and raising their arms, imploring God's mercy. "Amen! God have mercy," they moaned, their intensity swelling.

Pappaw opened his Bible. "But the fearful, and unbelieving, and the abominable . . ."

"But da fearful, and unbelieving, and da abominable . . ." the congregation echoed.

". . . and murderers, and whoremongers, and sorcerers, and idolaters, and all liars," Pappaw continued earnestly.

". . . and murderers, and whoremongers, and sorcerers, and idolaters, and all liars . . ." Like a mounting wave, their emotion grew.

". . . shall have their part in the lake which burneth with fire and brimstone: which is the second death." The sweat rolled down Pappaw's face and mixed with his heartfelt tears.

". . . shall have their part in da lake which burneth with fire and brimstone: which is da second death,"[2] shouted the parishioners.

"Amen!" Pappaw ended the Scripture reading with a shout.

"Amen! Preach it! Yes, Lawd!" The congregation's fervency surged to a crest.

Even though Lillie and her family were "high class" and could read and write, many of the other sharecroppers couldn't. And none of the share-croppers other than Pappaw had the luxury of owning a Bible. Pappaw's reading of his Bible was the Lord's word of hope for them each Lord's Day. They drank it in as Pappaw read the passage and explained how to apply it in their everyday life.

"Someday we will be rewarded for our sweat and our tears." Some of those tears were streaming now.

"Dat's right. We will!" the congregation called out.

"And nobody will turn us 'round!"

"Dat's true, preach it!"

"God's in charge and no masta' can stand in God's way when He decides to do something 'bout sin around us!" Pappaw thundered, his big black fist pounding the wooden pulpit.

"You right. Go on. Say it, preacher!" Handkerchiefs and rags were waving in the congregation to fan sweating faces. Eyes were closed and foreheads furrowed as they released the emotion that had been pent up all week.

"Let's run those spirits off our land because this is God's place, and we are God's people, and He don't want those Satan spirits here!"

"Dat's right! Let's do it! Let's go. God is with us!" Although unable to express all she felt, Lillie could sense the strength and unity gained in the call-and-response worship. She swayed with the bodies pressing against her and felt the emotions spilling from the people she worked and sweated with.

The choir led in a final rousing song:

> The gospel train's a-comin', I hear it just at hand,
> I hear the wheels rumblin' and rollin' through the land.
> Get on board little children, get on board little children,
> Get on board little children, there's room for many a-more.[3]

"Amen! Praise ya, Jesus." They bowed their heads, and Pappaw led them in a prayer of benediction.

The long walk home seemed short as the Johnson family sang together. Lillie skipped happily. She loved that Mammaw had time on Sundays to tell her stories from her childhood. Perhaps today she could hear another story.

Lillie sat at Mammaw's elbow as she rolled the dough and cut it into biscuits with a tin cup dipped in flour. "Mammaw," Lillie asked, "did your mama make biscuits for you?"

"Sure she did," Mammaw said, "but when I was a chile, my mama had ta live in the plantation house. She only was 'llowed ta come home on Sundays. So most times my sister made the biscuits."

"Why couldn't she live at home with you?"

"Those were slave days, chile. She was an ol' black mammy for the masta' and his mistress and all their children. She was on duty day and night. There was no time for her ta come home. Oh, we loved when she walked in the door on Sunday afternoon. She brought us some of the service pan, which was leftover food from her hard work that day. Mmm, mmm. We loved our cold victuals. Many times that was the best meal we got all week."

Lillie savored her biscuit a long time as she thought about Mammaw being a little girl whose mother was a slave. She decided she didn't have it so bad after all.

After dinner, Pappaw, Uncle George, and Daddy James dozed under the tree in front of the house, while the women cleaned up from the meal and prepared for another week.

Lillie loved evenings and Sundays when there was a break from the fieldwork and she could play with the neighbor girls. They drew a hopscotch grid in the dust in front of their house. Even though her friend Vicky was champion at hopscotch, Lillie hopped and skipped and did her best to keep up.

"Hop, skip, hop, skip." The girls played until they landed in a pile of helpless giggles.

When they were tired of hopscotch, they joined the boys. The boys drew a line in the dirt and lined up all the marbles as straight as possible. Taking a shooter, the children flicked it with their fingers, aiming at the line of marbles. As many marbles as they could shoot out across the line were theirs to keep. "Your turn!" Tucker told Lillie.

Lillie lay on her stomach and lined up her shiny blue marble with her eye. She flicked it hard with her finger. The marble whizzed right between two marbles. "Don't worry, Sis," Tucker encouraged, "you'll get one next time." Lillie ran to collect her shooter so she would be ready for her next turn.

After Vicky went home, Lillie watched over Tucker's shoulder as he and Walker played with their cardboard checker game. Buttons from Mammaw's button basket made dandy checkers. Lillie clamped her mouth shut as Tucker put his checker right in line to have Walker triple jump him.

"Gotcha," Walker crowed.

"I didn't see that move," Tucker said. He shook his head and squinted his eyes in concentration.

The next day it rained, and the girls from the sharecropping families in the neighborhood were invited to Cousin Ida's house. They crawled up a ladder and into the upstairs attic. They each had brought a corncob doll. "Now you be the mama, and I'll be the daddy," Lillie told Vicky. First they played church, then wedding. As Lillie was dancing her doll up the aisle toward her groom, the corncob doll broke in two.

"Let's have a funeral for her," Vicky said. They laid the corncob doll out nice and pretty in a box they found over by the window. Solemnly, they hauled the box down the rickety ladder and outside in the pouring rain. They quickly dug a hole along the fence by the edge of the property.

"Now you pray, Lillie, like your Pappaw."

So Lillie prayed. "Lawd Jesus, see us here."

"See us," moaned Vicky.

"Bless us as we bury our doll baby."

"Be with us, Lawd," Vicky added.

"Amen!"

"Amen!" Vicky said. Then she giggled. "You make good prayers like your Pappaw."

Carefully the girls covered the box with dirt. They hurried back inside to make another doll out of the corncobs drying in the attic. All too soon it was time to go home for supper.

chapter three

Into the Gutter

One fall morning a year later, Lillie and her brothers, now ages seven through eleven, awoke at five as usual. Although they had finished harvesting the cotton on their own farm, Daddy James had hired the children out to other plantations to earn some cash to pay the year's debt. Times were hard for everyone in the Depression of the 1930s, but the sharecroppers, dirt poor to begin with, suffered more than most.

Lillie walked with her brothers to a neighboring farm to work in their cotton field for the day. Since it was the very last picking of the season, their lumpy sacks of cotton filled as slowly as bread dough rises in a cold room. The bolls were few and far between.

"I'm so thirsty." Lillie bent over to strip another bush of its bolls. The sun bore down on them, and the children had soon drained the jug of water they had brought.

"Go ask for a drink at the plantation house," Tucker told her.

"Will they give me one?" Lillie asked dubiously.

"Of course they will."

Lillie stopped picking and stared at the grand old Southern house in the distance. Her dry, hot mouth reminded her of how thirsty she was. She heaved her bag off her shoulder and headed toward the house. She walked hesitantly up the sidewalk toward the large house, its stately white columns seeming to bar her entrance. She noticed a young man in the front yard washing his hair in a basin by the well. He looked up as Lillie approached, and his eyes narrowed when he saw her color.

"I-I was wondering . . ." Lillie stammered, looking down so she wouldn't meet the white boy's eyes. "I was wondering if you'd allow my brothers and me a drink. Just a little water, if you please. We're so hot."

The young man laughed. "Sure." He took his basin of greasy hair water and handed it to her.

Lillie's face flushed. "Thank you, sir." She had no choice but to answer him respectfully and take the water.

She hurried back to the field, water sloshing out of the sudsy basin. She could feel her face flame, and tears threatened to spill down her cheeks.

"That scoundrel," Tucker muttered when he saw the basin. "I'd like ta pour all this water down his throat." He threw the offensive water onto the field's edge. "We won't drink greasy hair water. We'll just go thirsty."

Their anger at the white boy's injustice made them pick faster. By the time they stopped that evening, their throats were parched and they felt woozy from the heat. When they got back to their cabin, Mammaw had cold water waiting for them.

School brought a welcome change of routine for the children when the field work was finished in the late fall. Black children had barely four months of classes to learn their year's worth of lessons. Lillie, Tucker, and Walker walked each day to their church house, which also served as their school.

Mammaw saved all the pretty calico sacks that the mill filled with their flour. She sorted through them and found three sacks of the same green calico pattern and three of red polka dots. From the sacks, she cut and sewed two new school dresses for Lillie.

Lillie couldn't wait to wear her flour sack dresses to school. The first morning she woke up early and had her dress on and buttoned up before she went to the kitchen. "Mammaw, do I have to wear stockings ta school? They're so scratchy."

"Of course you will," she said as she greased Lillie's hair with oil and tied pretty ribbons at the end of each row of braids. The boys stood impatiently just outside the door in their starched white shirts, black pants, and bowties.

"Goodbye," Mammaw called as they left the house. "Have a good day of school."

As soon as they were out of sight of the house, Lillie stopped. "Just a minute." She ran behind a bush and took off her shoes and stockings.

"Come on," Walker called. "We'll be late."

Lillie reappeared, carrying her stockings and shoes.

"Good idea," Walker said. The boys quickly stooped down, took off their shoes, and carried them to keep them clean.

As they rounded the last corner before the school, the children sat beside the road and put their shoes back on. Because Mammaw wouldn't see them, Lillie left her hated stockings rolled down.

The clapboard school, cleaned from top to bottom, stood waiting for the flurry of activity that would take place the coming months. Black children came from every direction and disappeared inside the tall open door. Lillie carried her tin pail inside and put it on a shelf above a row of hooks in the cloakroom. She hurried up the steps with her slate and into the one-room school.

"Good morning, Miss Lillie," the teacher greeted her.

Lillie stared at the tall, dignified woman in front of her. Her thick black hair was piled in a high coiffure on top of her head. Her skin shone. "G'mornin' Ma'am," Lillie said. *She's so beautiful and tall,* she thought. *And she talks so proper-like. I hope I look as pretty when I grow up.*

The teacher, Aunt Susie, led her to the front row of double wooden desks. "You may sit here." She gestured toward a seat. Aunt Susie wasn't really Lillie's aunt, but "Aunt" is what all the children called their schoolteachers.

Lillie laid her slate and pencil on the desk top. "Hi," she said, grinning broadly to the girl occupying the other half of the desk.

"Hello." Sutter slid over to make room for Lillie. "I'm lucky to have you beside me this year." Sutter lived about a mile from Lillie's house, and sometimes they played together on Sunday afternoons.

The desk seat squeaked as Lillie sat down. She lifted the lid in front of her and put her slate carefully inside. With so many children crowded into the small space, Lillie felt fortunate to get a desk and have a slate. She watched the teacher find seats for Walker and Tucker. Some of the older children sat on chairs around the edge of the room. Lillie was glad she and her brothers had their own slates so they could work independently.

"Lillie," Aunt Susie called. "Please recite the first paragraph of the Constitution of the United States."

Lillie's seat squeaked as she rose. She squinted and swallowed a lump that rose in her throat, trying to remember what she had memorized the year before. "We the People of the United States, in order to form a more perfect Union, establish Justice, insure domestic Tranquility, provide for the common defense, promote the general Welfare, and secure the Blessings of Liberty to ourselves and our Posterity, do ordain and establish this Constitution for the United States of America." She sat down.

"Very good, Lillie. I can see you love your country," Aunt Susie said.

Lillie nodded. She loved everything but the fact that she wasn't treated like the white people.

At lunchtime, Lillie and Sutter took their tin pails and joined Lillie's friend Vicky and the other girls under the big shade tree. Lillie slowly ate her boiled egg, then unwrapped her biscuit. Lillie loved the molasses her mother had spread generously on it.

As soon as their lunches were eaten, Sutter hopped up. "Come on," she said, pulling Lillie to her feet. "Let's go play hopscotch." The girls joined the line of other girls in front of the squares drawn in the dust.

"Hop, hop, skip, hop." Their shoes sang as they hopped from one square to another, trying not to make any mistakes.

The boys sat on the ground with their jacks and ball. *Bounce, bounce, grab.* The boys leaned closer as they focused on getting the correct number of jacks with each bounce of the ball. Soon it was time to go back into school for another study period.

On the way home from school, Lillie walked fast to keep up with her brothers. "I think we should stop and pick some blackberries ta sell," she said.

Tucker glanced down at her. "We don't have anything ta put 'em in."

"We got our lunch buckets," Walker said.

"Good idea," Tucker said. "Let's surprise Mammaw with 'em."

The children scoured the fencerows for blackberries. Pulling the briars aside, Lillie stretched on her tiptoes to pick the elusive fruit. The first berry plunked into the bottom of her lunch pail. Lillie popped the next one into her mouth. The sun-warmed sweetness trickled down her throat. "Mmm!" she said. Before long, more berries were going into her mouth than into her pail.

"Lillie!" Tucker teased. "You eating all your profit? My bucket's half full. How 'bout yours?"

Lillie reddened. "Well, I don't have as many as you, but I'll hurry." She quit eating and picked faster. The briars caught on her skirt. The sun beat down on them.

"Done!" Tucker grinned with satisfaction. "Want me ta help ya, Lillie?"

Lillie nodded. Soon the three pails held rounded mounds of berries.

"Think Mammaw will let us sell these?" Lillie wondered.

"Of course she will," Walker said. "They need our money ta make Pappaw's yearly loan payment."

Lillie sighed. "Wouldn't it be nice ta be able ta keep some money for ourselves?" she asked wistfully.

"Silly," Walker said. "Pappaw needs it. We don't."

Their feet hurried along the dusty road toward home. At the end of their lane, Lillie sat down and rolled her stockings back up so Mammaw wouldn't know.

"Mammaw," Lillie called as she burst through the door. "We got some blackberries. May we take 'em ta town ta sell?"

Mammaw rubbed the fresh piece of newspaper she had just pasted on the wall to cover a hole where she had removed an old brittle piece. Lillie stared at all the newspaper glued in a random pattern covering the ugly wooden walls. Would they ever be able to have pretty papered walls like the plantation house on the hill?

"I don't know why not," Mammaw said.

"Let's go." Lillie opened the door.

"Don't be late for supper!" Mammaw called after them.

As they neared the town, Lillie stared at the beautiful tree-lined streets. She looked in the windows of "White Only" stores, knowing she would get in terrible trouble if she set her foot inside. And after all, her family had no money to spend in these wealthy stores anyway, even if they had been permitted to shop there. *I wish I could go in an' just look,* she thought.

"I'm thirsty," Walker said. "I'm stoppin' ta get a drink." Across the street two water fountains stood in front of the town hall. The one on the left was a ceramic white sink with shiny taps. "WHITE," said the sign above it. "What would happen if I drank from this one?" Walker asked, pointing as he scampered across the street.

"Don't!" Lillie's eyes widened in fright. She had heard the stories of what happened to black people who did things the whites didn't like.

"I get tired of people thinkin' I'm not as good 'cause I'm black," Walker growled. "Someday, people are gonna respect me in spite of my color."

"Just don't buck the system," Tucker warned. "You can't change it any more than you can change your skin color."

Lillie glanced to the right of the gleaming ceramic drinking fountain. She cringed when she saw the small tin sink with a rusty spout for drinking. "COLORED," read the sign above it. Resigned, Walker walked over and drank his fill of the rust-flecked water. "Yuck!" he said, spitting his last mouthful on the ground.

After he rejoined his siblings, they walked on down the sidewalk. A white man and his wife were coming the opposite direction. The three children instinctively stepped down into the mucky gutter to allow the white couple to pass. They knew they would be cursed and possibly arrested if they blocked the sidewalk. To resist the unfair social system would only make heartache for their family. After the couple had passed, the children bent down and wiped the sludge from their shoes.

"Ugh! That stinks," Lillie complained.

"Hush," Tucker said.

"Don't ya ever get tired of bein' treated like an animal?" Walker hissed.

"You don't want a night in prison to remind you of your position, do ya?" Tucker asked angrily.

Walker shook his head.

"Then behave like a gen'leman, like Mammaw taught you."

The street ahead was lined with mansions. Trees waved their green branches above the manicured lawns behind the black iron gates. The children stared in awe. Timidly they walked up to the grand mahogany door of the first house and raised the brass knocker. The door opened a crack. "What do you niggers want?" A thin, pinched face frowned at them. Lillie stared at the delicate lace edging the jade collar that rose high on the gray-haired woman's white throat.

Tucker cleared his throat. "W-would you like to buy some blackberries?"

"Not if you picked them!" The door slammed in their faces.

Walker spat on the sidewalk as they left. "Walker," Tucker warned. "Mammaw wouldn't want you to treat anyone like that!"

Walker just snorted his disgust.

They tried the next house, then the next. Nobody wanted their berries.

"Should we jes' go on home?" Lillie's shoulders drooped.

"Let's try one more house," Tucker encouraged.

The last house on the street stood tall and regal. The children walked between the two white pillars up a flight of marble steps to knock on the door. "Hello?" A friendly man's face appeared at the door. "What can I do for you children?"

"We'd like ta sell our berries. Would ya buy 'em?" Tucker held out his bucketful.

"Teresa?" the man called to the woman inside. "Do you want some blackberries?"

"Sure," she called back. "I don't have time to go pick them myself."

"I'll go dump them in the kitchen," the man said. He took their full buckets into the house. A moment later he returned with their empty lunch buckets. Lillie shuffled her feet as the man dug in his pocket. He counted out ten pennies and pressed them into Tucker's hand. Then ten more pennies into Walker's, then Lillie's.

"Thank ya, sir," Tucker said for all of them. Their berries had brought a good price.

Lillie gazed beyond the nice white man to the beautiful sitting room. She longed to sit on the stuffed chairs, feel the crackling fire in the spacious fireplace, and eat from the beautiful pieces of fine bone china decorating the hutch.

The lady sat on one of the plush chairs with a book in one hand and a bottle of soda in the other. "Someday," Lillie murmured, "someday I will have all that." She forced her gaze away and turned to follow her brothers back down the street, back to the country plantation where they eked out their living one day at a time.

"We done good today," Tucker said, holding out the thirty cents to Mammaw when they returned home.

"Good for you," Mammaw said. She kissed them each on the tops of their heads. "How would we make it without you?"

chapter four

Bunion Stew

Autumn brought cooler weather. The longer evenings allowed more time for socializing. The darkness inside the windowless shack drove the Johnson family to their front porch most evenings where they listened to the evening chorus of crickets and watched the sun set on the horizon.

"Pappaw, why do all the shacks on the plantations have green painted posts?" Lillie asked one evening as she stared at their porch posts.

Pappaw smiled. "Some of our friends say it's ta look like water. They say haunts don't wanna cross water, so the green color makes 'em stay away."

Lillie's eyes grew wide. "Haunts?" she asked. A shiver ran down her back. She knew many Negroes saw haunts, and she didn't want to.

Pappaw saw fear in her eyes. "I don't believe in haunts, chile. My Jesus don't 'llow haunts to His children. I like to believe the green helps keep the flies away."

"It don't seem to work very well," Lillie grumbled as she swatted at another fly. Then she hopped up. "Let's sing!"

Pappaw smiled. "Run get my accordion."

Lillie skipped into the dark house and crept to the corner by Pappaw's bed. She felt along the wall until she touched the hard accordion case. She found the two latches that held it shut and popped open the creaky case. In the dim light, Lillie saw Pappaw's beloved instrument lying on red velvet. She lifted it gently and carried it to the front porch.

Pappaw took it in his hands and positioned the leather strap around his shoulders. His fingers played the buttons as he pumped the bellows and sang,

> Jes' think of His goodness to you,
> Yes, think of His goodness to you,
> Though storms o'er thee sweep,
> He is able ta keep;
> O think of His goodness to you![1]

Lillie clapped her hands and tapped her feet to the music of the accordion. Songs made her feel like her problems disappeared. They made the world seem right. She could imagine her life was just as good as Mister Big Ike's daughter Sue's life on the hill.

As the shadows began to lengthen late one afternoon, Daddy James paused on his way up the porch steps, skillfully dodging the broken one. "There's my girl," Daddy James said to Lillie, who was playing with her doll on the porch. "How'd you like ta go to the creek this evening with your brothers to set up a line ta catch a big snappin' turtle?"

"Oh, yes!" Lillie jumped up and down, clapping her hands in delight. "Then we'll make bunion stew, right, Daddy James?"

Daddy James chuckled. "I tell you, if you children can catch a big one, we'll make soup and have a real neighborhood social."

Tucker found a bucket and some scraps of meat that Mammaw said he could use.

"Race ya to the big log!" Walker set off at a run. Tucker soon caught up with Walker, but Lillie's short legs couldn't keep up. When they reached the creek, the boys plopped down beside the fallen tree to wait for her.

Tucker pulled a line out of his pocket, and Walker fished some meat scraps out of the bucket and baited a big fish hook. "Think this hook is strong enough?" Walker tried to bend it with his hands.

"Better be, but they'll do their best ta bite it off." Tucker tied the hook tightly to the string.

"Shh! Let's go," Walker whispered. The three of them crept onto the mossy tree bridge and crouched down. "Now look careful' and see if you see any turtles swimmin'."

They scanned the murky water as it swirled around the log. "There," Tucker whispered, pointing to some ripples close to the log. "Looks like a big one."

They threw their baited line into the water and secured it to the log. Knowing the turtles wouldn't come out until they were gone, they left their bait there for the night. Putting one foot in front of the other, they balanced on the log as they crept back to the bank. They hid the bucket in some brush and hurried home. "Why don't we just stay and see if we catch one?" Lillie asked.

"Turtles are night feeders," Tucker said. "They won't come lookin' for the bait for a few hours yet. Once they find out they've been hooked, they'll move close to the shore to try ta hide. That makes 'em easy to pull out in the morning. We'll come back and check once it's light tomorrow."

Lillie felt too excited to sleep, but the next thing she knew, the morning sunlight streamed through the cracks in the bedroom walls.

Daddy James, Walker, and Tucker were waiting to go to the creek. Lillie stuffed her mouth with a biscuit before hurrying out to join them. "Ready ta go?" Daddy James asked.

Lillie nodded. She took big steps to keep up with Daddy James and her brothers, and soon they reached the fallen log bridge where they had put their line in the evening before. "Look at all the ripples!" Tucker exclaimed. "Somethin's on the line." Grabbing the bucket from the brush, they hurried out onto the log.

"Careful now," Daddy James warned. "Them snappers will make you minus a finger mighty quick. Keep your hands away from him."

Carefully, Daddy James reeled in the line. Thrashing on the end of the line was a big brown turtle. "He's a snapper, that's for sure," Daddy James cried. "Look at his dull shell."

"He's ugly," Walker wrinkled his brown nose.

"Yep," Daddy James said, "they don't have pretty markings on their shell."

"How much ya think he weighs?" Tucker eyed the turtle apprehensively.

"Gotta be twenty pounds at least," Daddy James grunted, holding him a safe distance from his body. He carefully guided the line into the bucket and cut the line with a knife he drew from his pocket.

The children clustered around the bucket. "Snap, snap, snap!" The turtle lashed out at his confinement.

Daddy James pulled the turtle's head out with the hook still in it. He clubbed the head sharply with a stick, stunning the turtle. Quickly he twisted off the neck and threw the head out into the brush. "Stay away from that head," Daddy James warned. "Reflex keeps them jaws active long after they've been cut off. I don't want it biting none of you."

Holding the carcass by a leg, Daddy James carried it home. With a stout cord, he hung it in the tree to keep it out of reach of animals. Leaving it there all night allowed the blood to drain out, making it easier to cut up the next day.

Tucker and Walker spread the word throughout the neighborhood and among the shacks down in the river bottoms that everyone was welcome the next evening for a neighborhood social.

In the morning, Pappaw and Daddy James dug a hole in front of their shack and filled it with a pile of coal. Patiently, Daddy James coaxed a small fire to burn. They hung a pot over the fire. Daddy James cut the big turtle down from the tree. The children crowded close. "Ew! Daddy James." Lillie wrinkled her small brown nose. "Will we really eat that thing?"

Daddy James chuckled. " 'Course we will! Turtle meat's tasty. Don't ya remember eatin' turtle before?"

Lillie shook her head. She wasn't too sure about all this.

They watched as Daddy James laid the headless, bloodless carcass on its back, and—with a sharp knife—cut between the shells and lifted off the bottom one. Removing the entrails from the top shell, he discarded them. Next, he skinned the legs, neck, and tail, cutting these from the body and laying them aside. He trimmed the yellow fat from the meat and discarded that as well.

"Look, children," he said. "Two nice pieces of meat in this top shell."

"Oh," Lillie exclaimed. The boys just nodded.

Daddy James broke off the few small bones covering these chunks. He removed them and cut up the meat. He added the legs, tail, and neck. All afternoon the meat bubbled in the pot over the coals. By evening, Lillie's stomach growled. It sure smelled good. Daddy James added cabbage, corn, peas, beans, carrots, and potatoes, and his famous bunion stew kept cooking.

While the stew simmered, Pappaw and Daddy James cut down a tall, straight sapling. After stripping off the tender branches, they dragged it a little distance from the steaming stew. Carefully they greased the tree all over with petroleum jelly. Together they dug another big hole, tied a bag onto the very top of the newly greased post, and lifted it up. While Daddy James held the pole straight, Pappaw filled in the dirt around it. Now the post stood sturdy and tall for games that evening.

The day dragged for Lillie. She paced the front porch as she watched the preparations. Her friends and cousins were coming from the bottoms. She knew her grandparents had invited only the "sanctified" neighbors. It would be a clean party with singing, laughter, and games.

Lillie watched the dirt road until the neighbors started to arrive. She skipped out the lane. "Hi, Ada," she called. "Hurry! Daddy James's stew is ready."

The neighbors trickled in, all of them bringing their own tin bowls and spoons since the Johnsons had no extra. No one minded sitting on the ground around the fire. Lillie saw one little boy eyeing the soup. Daddy James wiped his sweaty forehead as he stirred in some flour to thicken it. At the very last he sprinkled in some cooked noodles and added some hardboiled eggs and then pronounced it ready.

"Let's pray." Pappaw bowed his head. "Almighty God, we thank ya for this day."

"Amen!" the people shouted.

"For your provisions, we thank ya."

"Yes, Lawd!"

"Give us love for each other and love for our haters!"

"Amen, Lawd, give us love." The spoons clattered on the tin bowls as they raised them in worship.

"Amen, and thank ya, Lawd," Pappaw ended.

"Amen!"

Daddy James was ladling delicious turtle soup into each bowl. Lillie's stomach was growling. At long last, she held out her bowl for Daddy James to fill. She lifted the spoon and took a little taste. "Mmm!" she said aloud. It tasted every bit as good as it smelled. The meat was tender and vegetables soft and seasoned to perfection. She smiled at Daddy James. "I guess I do like turtle stew."

Daddy James chuckled.

"Good stew, James," Uncle Eddy said. Spoons scraped tin bowls as everyone lapped up the delicious stew. Soon it was gone.

Pappaw clapped his hands for attention. "Now it's time for some fun." He pointed to the pole they had erected that day.

Nods and chuckles spread among the folks. Greased pole climbing provided lots of fun. At the top hung a prize in a bag. Tonight it was a piece of cake.

"Any volunteers ta try for the prize?" The teams of young boys clamored for the chance, slipping and sliding their way up as far as they could. The slippery grease made it hard to get a good grip. They could scarcely make any progress, but still they tried. One boy would climb on another's shoulders and try to hold on tight to the pole. Then a third would climb up both of them and try to hold on while a fourth and sometimes a fifth boy climbed.

"Go, Tucker! Go, Walker!" Lillie shouted at the red-faced boys halfway up the post. But soon they slid back down without cake in their hands. Other boys tried with no success. Finally, Mammaw brought out beautiful layered cakes. She cut generous slices and served them to everyone.

As dusk settled, Pappaw brought out his accordion; Uncle George, his harmonica and guitar; and another neighbor, his Jew's harp. They all sang in unison, clapping their hands and tapping their feet on the hard-packed dirt.

> Oh, how I love Jesus,
> Oh, how I love Jesus,
> Oh, how I love Jesus,
> Because He first loved me.[2]

Swatting away the mosquitoes, Lillie watched the fireflies blink on, then off. She joined the singing as darkness descended. Her heart felt light as she sang her troubles away.

It was late before anyone headed for home. Lillie kept waving long after the last friend had vanished in the darkness. Then she turned slowly back toward the house and sat by the fire, hugging her knees.

Daddy James filled his cast iron pot with water and begin to wash it, while Mammaw swept the ground around the fire pit. Daddy James sloshed the dirty water on the fire. It sizzled and smoked. Pappaw stirred the ashes with a blackened stick, then spread them out so no spark would escape. Lillie sat by the fire till the glow from the last ember died out, trying to hold onto the excitement of the day. She hated to see the evening end. Daddy James poured the rest of his water over the coals and they headed for their shack.

The next morning, Lillie walked with Daddy James to the mule pen. They planned to hitch the mules to the plow to begin tilling the dry cotton stalks into the soil. "Daddy James," Lillie gasped, "the mule is gone!"

"What?" Daddy James groaned. "Where could he have gone this time? Mister Big Ike is gonna be upset at me for letting the mule loose again." Another loss for Mister Ike meant another loss for him and Pappaw. To get their field ready for a new crop, they needed to plow soon, and they couldn't plow without a mule. "We'd better head up the road an' see if we can find the bugger."

They followed the hoof marks up the dusty lane where they ended at the road's edge. "Which way did that stubborn mule head?" Daddy James muttered.

"I bet he started ta walk toward town," Lillie offered, eager to help.

Together they started down the road. No mule. A wagon rattled up beside them. "Need some help?" asked a neighbor headed to Canton.

"Lost my mule," Daddy James said. "Mind if I ride with ya so I can look for 'im along the road?"

"Nope. Don't mind 'tall. Hop on." Daddy James swung Lillie into the wagon and climbed in after her.

"Nice day." The neighbor tried to make conversation.

"Yeah," Daddy James grunted. But all the time he was looking for the mule. They clip-clopped the three miles to town without seeing any sign of the animal.

As the wagon turned onto the main street, Lillie stared. Tall brick buildings connected to form a facade up one side and down the other. The streets bustled with people, horses, and wagons. Lillie's spine tingled, and she leaned forward in her seat so as not to miss any of the action.

"Whoa," the neighbor called, coming to a halt in front of the hardware store. He climbed down and tied the reins to the hitching post. "I've got a few things ta get in here."

Daddy James vaulted over the edge of the wagon. "I'll jes' be a minute," he said to Lillie. "You stay here with the wagon. Since I'm in town anyway, I want ta get some supplies I need ta finish my fieldwork."

As Lillie sat waiting, she watched the busy street as wagons rumbled, horses clopped, and children yelled and rolled hoops with sticks in the dirt. One boy turned to look at her. When he saw her dark skin, he stuck out his tongue at her. Lillie looked the other way. Tears stung her eyes. She wanted to be thick-skinned and not let him see how he had hurt her.

"Lillie?" a soft voice beside the wagon made Lillie jump.

"Sue! What are you doin' here?" Lillie asked.

"Sorry to startle you, Lillie, but I wanted to see you." Sue smoothed her straight blonde hair with her fingers.

Lillie gazed at her neighbor longingly. "Don't let your Daddy Ike see ya talkin' to a nigger."

"Shh!" Sue said, putting her finger to her lip. "I don't think of you that way. I wish we could be friends. I can't stand it that our color keeps us apart."

Lillie felt circles of warmth around her heart. "We can be friends anyway," she said shyly. "Friends in our hearts."

Sue smiled. "I like that."

Lillie gained more courage. "Sometimes I envy you in your beautiful house on the hill." Her face flushed at the admission.

Sue grimaced. "It's lonely being the only daughter of a plantation owner. Mother and Father don't even talk to each other most of the time. All I do is sit and stitch on my sampler and do other boring ladylike things."

Lillie stared at Sue, as new thoughts swirled in her mind.

"Sometimes," Sue continued, "I sneak to my bedroom and watch your family out my window. I listen to your singing. I envy *your* happiness. All of you are a big happy family, enjoying each other. You get to work and play together. I have no one."

Lillie's mouth dropped open. She had never dreamed Sue would envy her.

Suddenly a voice yelled, "Sue, what are you doing? Quit talking to that nigger and get over here."

"I've got to run," Sue said. "See you later." She waved and her green taffeta skirt swirled as she hurried down the street and hopped into the surrey beside her father.

Lillie heard angry voices, and her heart hurt for Sue, the lonely plantation girl. "I'm sorry ta get you in trouble, Sue," she whispered.

As she watched, a cloud of dust appeared out of nowhere. Her eyes grew wide as she watched a machine come purring down the street. "What's that?" she asked fearfully.

"That's an auto-mo-bile," Daddy James pronounced carefully behind her. "It's a wonderful invention. It doesn't need any horses ta run. I had me some drivin' lessons when I was helpin' in the neighbor's fields last week."

The car stopped in a cloud of dust across the street and a dapper man got out. "Who's that?" Lillie asked.

"He's Mr. Noble, a plantation owner. I hear he treats his sharecroppers nice an' fair. I'd like ta work for him someday, 'specially on days like today. My profit's gone all 'cause that dumb mule got loose."

The neighbor came out of the store and leaped on the wagon. "All ready?" he asked.

"You bet we are," Daddy James grumbled. "Need to find that critter."

Clucking to his horses, the neighbor turned the wagon around and headed back toward the country. Lillie and her Daddy James scanned the fields for any sign of the missing mule. "There he is!" Lillie shouted. She leaped off the wagon as soon as it came to a halt. She crept up beside the mule and touched his side, then slid her hand up the side of his head and grabbed his halter. Daddy James was right behind her.

"You rascal," he said, jerking on the bridle. "How'd you get out anyway? Let's head for home. I need ta get somethin' done today yet."

Together they traipsed the long mile home. "At least we found the mule," Lillie said, trying to ease her father's mind.

"Yeah, glad I don't have ta report this to Mister Big Ike." Daddy James shook his head. "But can't get ahead on days like today."

chapter five

Bathed in Molasses

The sugarcane leaves rustled in the fall breeze. Harvest involved long hours of cutting the tall stalks with a machete-like knife. Lillie and her brothers then stripped the leaves from the stalks, leaving a stiff, heavy trunk of cane. Lillie's fingers were soon cut and bleeding from the sharp edges of the leaves.

Tucker and Walker lifted the long stalks into the wagon. Tomorrow Uncle George or Pappaw would drive the cane to the mill where the stalks were squeezed so the liquid could run out. Lillie licked her lips when she thought of the molasses they would bring back home. They had used all of last year's already and Lillie was longing for the sweet, musky syrup on Mammaw's fluffy biscuits.

"Uncle George," Lillie asked her uncle early the next morning, "can we ride to the mill with you?"

"Why, sure, why don't ya bring Walker and Tucker too. It's a great day for a ride." Uncle George carefully arranged the stalks of cane on the back of the wagon and tucked empty molasses jars all around them. They would exchange the empty jars for full ones at the mill.

Lillie lifted her foot high to climb onto the wagon step. She hefted herself up, and Walker and Tucker jumped in after her. Uncle George leaped onto the wagon seat and slapped the reins, and the horse clomped down the lane and out onto the highway. The swaying of the wagon made Lillie drowsy, but she was determined to stay awake until they got to the mill.

When they arrived at the ramshackle wooden shed with its brick chimney poking out the top, a number of other wagons were gathered, waiting for their loads of sugarcane to be processed. Uncle George and Lillie's brothers heaped the stiff cane stalks onto piles. They waited all morning until the mill operators were ready for their pile.

Lillie watched as the stalks were fed into the extractor and the "chews" were discarded. The raw molasses was collected in a huge kettle and placed over a wood fire. After it was boiled down, the thick syrup was poured into the clean jars and left to cool before being carried to the waiting wagon. Uncle George paid the mill men by giving them an eighth portion of the molasses.

The ride home was jubilant as everyone sang and clapped together:

> Swing low, sweet chariot, comin' for to carry me home,
> Swing low, sweet chariot, comin' for to carry me home.
> I looked over Jordan and what do I see
> Comin' for to carry me home?
> A band of angels—[1]

"Uncle George, watch out!"

Lillie gaped as an automobile coming toward them careened around the corner in a cloud of dust. Its driver obviously did not notice the wagon. "That automobile is gonna hit us!" Lillie shrieked. The children dove to the wagon floor as the automobile rammed into the wagon. The wagon splintered in two. They sat stunned.

Slowly, they rose from the floor of the splintered wagon bed. Dark, sticky liquid from the broken molasses jars covered them and dripped to the ground. The driver shook his fist at them. "You niggers get off this road!" he yelled through his window. The driver backed the automobile, swerved into the oncoming lane, and roared away.

"Everyone all right?" Uncle George asked shakily as he hurried to the back of the wagon to check on his niece and nephews.

"Yes, but we're all sticky!" Lillie wailed.

Uncle George shook his head. "That driver should be turned in to the authorities for wrecking into us." He helped the children out of the wrecked wagon one by one. They looked at each other pathetically. Their eyes shone white through the gooey mask.

"What will Mammaw say?" Tucker asked. "We ruined all her molasses for the year."

They started for home on foot, slogging in goo as they walked the short distance to their shack. Mammaw opened the door, took one look, and started shrieking, "Look at all that blood! Look at all that blood!" She wrung her hands, screeching her alarm to the skies.

"It's awright, Mammaw," Uncle George said. "It's just molasses. We ain't hurt."

Mammaw stopped screaming. "You ain't hurt? Promise?"

Uncle George nodded. "Yes, we be fine. But all our year's molasses is down the front of us and all over the road by the wagon. All ruined. And the wagon split right down the middle. All in splinters." They stared sadly at Mammaw, their shoulders slumped in despair.

"Well, I'm just praising de Lawd everyone's all right. I don't care 'bout no molasses. Y'all look terrible." Mammaw hurried out to the porch and hauled the galvanized tub down from the wall and filled it with water. "Git in, wash yourselves off." One by one, the children scrubbed themselves in the old tin tub. Mammaw kept running to the well for fresh water. The water became black with the sweet-smelling syrup, but the fresh water and soap rinsed off most of the dripping molasses.

Pappaw came in from working in the field. He paused on the top step of the cabin and sniffed. "What do I smell?" he asked.

"Jus' molasses," Mammaw said. "All over everything."

That night Pappaw, Daddy James, and Uncle George took a neighbor's wagon to bring their wrecked one home. "I'm 'fraid it'll take some time to get this one patched up," Daddy James said, discouraged. "And one more loss for us."

Pappaw laid his work-worn brown hand on Daddy James's slumped shoulder. "Let's not fret, now. The good Lawd knows just what we need, an' He'll be givin' it to us at jes' the right time." Seeing the anger on Daddy James's face, he added, "The Good Book say vengeance belongs ta God, not ta us. We gotta love folks even when they do bad things; that's the only way ta have peace down in the heart. We gotta praise de Lawd!"

chapter six

"We're Moving!"

The next morning Lillie sat on the front porch, thinking about Sue and hoping she hadn't gotten into trouble for talking to her. As she kicked absentmindedly at the broken step, she saw a cloud of dust swirling down the dirt road. Coming toward her was the same automobile she had seen in town recently. It drove in the lane to their farm. "Daddy James!" Lillie slammed the door behind her as she ran into the house. "There's an automobile coming up the lane. Who do you think it is, Daddy James? Is it the same one we saw the other day?" She bounced on her toes in excitement.

"Hmm! I don't know." Daddy James peered out the front door, then brushed biscuit crumbs off the front of his shirt before stepping onto the porch.

"Are you Mr. James Johnson?" the man in the car asked as he parked and got out. His white pants and matching vest and shiny shoes contrasted with James's plaid shirt, patched overalls, and bare feet.

"Yes, sir." Daddy James swallowed hard. "Is somethin' wrong?"

Oh, boy. I hope Daddy James didn't do anything ta offend him. Why else would he come ta talk ta Daddy James? Lillie's heart pounded.

The man chuckled. "No, I came out to offer you a job. I'm Mr. Noble." The man held out his hand, and Daddy James hesitantly offered his.

"What can I do for ya?" Daddy James's voice faltered.

"My chauffeur left me last week, and I need another," Mr. Noble said. "I asked around town and found out you're a highly respected black man who knows something about driving automobiles. I would like to offer you this job. I would pay you well."

Daddy James stared. He could hardly believe the offer. However, it wasn't uncommon for one plantation owner to "steal" good workers from another. Many times a whole family was hired because it was cheap labor for the plantation owner. "I dunno what to say. I'd like ta take the job," Daddy James said boldly, "but I'd have one condition."

Mr. Noble frowned, taken aback. "What's that?" It was unheard of for blacks to make conditions for a job agreement. Lillie's heart sped up again. What if Mr. Noble had her daddy arrested?

Daddy James cleared his throat. "I don' want my wife and children workin' in your fields."

Mr. Noble laughed. "It's a deal. I'm hiring you. I won't force your family to work the fields, but I would like your wife to help out in my plantation house."

"That's a deal," Daddy James smiled broadly, white teeth gleaming. The white man and black man shook hands.

As the automobile drove out the lane, Lillie watched Daddy James throw back his head. *"Wooo-hoo!"* came his exultant yell. Then he turned and ran toward the house.

Daddy James burst through the door with Lillie right behind him. "We're movin'!" he shouted. He caught Mama Belle by the waist and twirled her around with him. Lillie had to grin at Daddy James's delight, but at the same time her palms started to sweat and her stomach felt unsettled.

Mama Belle gasped. "You mean leave Pappaw and Mammaw?"

Lillie's eyes grew wide. Her breath came in short gasps. She hadn't thought about that.

"Yes." Daddy James said. "Life'll be better for us on Mr. Noble's farm. You won't have ta work in the fields, and the children won't either. It be fine, you jes' wait and see!"

Mama Belle pursed her lips in a thin line and swallowed hard to get rid of the lump in her throat. She started packing to leave the only home she had ever known.

"Why are we leaving Pappaw and Mammaw?" Lillie tried hard to keep her voice steady. She could tell Mama Belle supported Daddy James, but all that seemed safe and familiar was crumbling into little pieces, and she wanted to know why.

"Your Daddy James wants a better life." Mama Belle carefully wrapped their few possessions and laid them in a crate.

"It can't be better if we're far away from Pappaw and Mammaw," Lillie persisted hotly. She stifled a sob, determined to convince her Mama they were making a mistake. "And what about Sue up on the hill? She's my friend. I'll miss her too."

"We won't be far away," Mama Belle told her. "You'll get used to it. We can still see Pappaw and Mammaw sometimes. Hurry now, get your things."

Tucker and Walker helped Daddy James carry everything out to the wagon. Pappaw and Mammaw followed the family outside. "We surely will miss all of you." Pappaw's voice was husky. "I wanna pray for you before ya leave."

Daddy James removed his straw hat and folded his hands across his chest. He bowed his head, not in prayer, but in respect. Mama Belle motioned to the children to bow theirs as well.

"Lawd, be near these your children now," Pappaw prayed.

"Yes, Lawd," Mammaw murmured. Her dark face was scrunched up to keep the tears away.

"Keep them from danger and that ol' evil one," Pappaw said.

"Keep 'em, Lawd."

"May their lives prosper, and may they all learn ta love you. Amen!"

"Amen!" everyone chorused.

Pappaw and Mammaw hugged each one in turn, and Pappaw swung them onto the wagon. "Now, hear ye." He shook his finger. "We'd better see some more of you."

"We'll be back," Mama Belle promised.

Nobody spoke. The horses clip-clopped down the dirt road. Lillie watched the dust billow behind them. *Do we have ta move away?* Her heart hurt, but she knew black folks had to do what they could to improve their lives when the chance came. She just wished Daddy James's chance to make good didn't mean leaving Mammaw and Pappaw. The harder she tried not to cry, the bigger the lump in her throat grew.

"Is this it?" Mama Belle's eyebrows arched as Daddy James pulled up in front of a tiny shack.

" 'Fraid so," Daddy James said apologetically. "It's smaller than I thought. I shoulda asked Mr. Noble 'bout where we'd live."

"Why would we expect anythin' better?" Mama Belle's voice was bitter. "Why'd we ever expect livin' in anythin' better?"

Lillie pulled her ragged coat closer. "Someday I will," Lillie said aloud in a thin little voice. No one heard her.

The family gazed at the tiny shack. Its weathered logs sagged, and the edges of the wood hung in splinters. Wooden shakes covered half of the roof. Would the tiny shanty hold their whole family? "Well," Mama Belle said with a sigh, "let's go see if we fit."

Tucker, Walker, and Lillie jumped off the wagon. Piling their arms full of pillows and the straw ticks that served as their mattresses, they followed Daddy James as he pushed open the door. Cracks in the plank floor gaped wide enough to reveal the ground underneath. The walls had newspaper pasted over the planks. But some of the walls still had big cracks. Lillie smashed her nose against the wall and peered through the crack with one eye. "Daddy James!" she cried. "I can see the field through the walls."

"That's sure not gonna hold out the winter winds." Mama Belle shook her head.

They carried their belongings into the small shack. Lillie helped fix the beds. She held back the tears that threatened to squeeze out of her eyes. "I don't like it here," she wavered. She looked up to see sky through the ceiling.

Mama Belle hugged her close. "We'll get used ta it. Soon it'll be home. Daddy James'll work on it. It'll soon be chinked an' dry. It'll be cozy this winter." Her voice held determination.

But Daddy James didn't have time to do anything. The next morning, Mr. Noble pulled up in his beautiful car. "I need to go check on my crops on the far end of my plantation," he said. "I was hoping you would be ready to start work." The plantations were often as big as towns, so Lillie knew Daddy James could be gone a long time.

"I am ready," Daddy James said. He took his place behind the wheel, and off they went. Daddy James looked proud as he motored off carefully.

Lillie helped Mama Belle finish settling in as well as they could. "This shack is so dirty," Mama Belle muttered. She turned to Tucker. "Take the metal bucket and bring in some fresh water."

Lillie trailed behind her brother to the well. Tucker set the dented pail on the ground and lifted the well lid. Peering down, he grabbed a rope and pulled. Tucker fastened his bucket to the hook on the end of the rope and lowered it. Lillie heard a splash as the bucket hit the water. Soon it appeared with fresh water sloshing out.

They carried it back to the shack. Mama Belle and Lillie scrubbed the floor with lye, making it feel clean and usable. It didn't take long to put away the family's few belongings. Lillie wandered around the property, wondering dismally how long it would be before it felt like home.

Late that night, Daddy James drove in. "Whew! What a day," he said. "Not only did we drive across the whole plantation, but we also drove to the barber. I waited while Mr. Noble had himself a haircut. Then he had business at the bank. So I drove him there. I never thought 'bout how much waiting I'd be doing. But I ain't complainin'. It's a good job."

The next morning, Mama Belle and Lillie dressed quickly. Mrs. Noble was expecting both of them this morning. "Let me drive you to the plantation house," Daddy James said, leading them out to the car.

Lillie crawled into the back seat beside Mama Belle. She smoothed the white leather seats and leaned back as the car seemed to fly over the road. Daddy James stopped at an intersection to see if there were any other cars. Then he eased forward. "Stop, Daddy James!" Lillie yelled. A car was careening around the corner.

The car lurched as Daddy James braked. "My, that car is in a hurry!" Mama Belle exclaimed.

The driver slowed only slightly at the crossroad, then sped on in a cloud of dust.

"White men," Daddy James muttered. "It rankles me that I have to stop for 'em. Why can't they watch where they're goin'? They act like we coloreds owe 'em somethin'."

"Next time you show them a thing or two," Lillie declared stoutly.

Daddy James shook his head. "Wouldn't work. If we had an accident, it'd be my fault. No questions asked. Lillie, always remember, accept your social class. Don't fight it."

Lillie's lips tightened. She didn't tell Daddy James, but somehow she planned on being respected by white people someday.

The grand automobile purred its way up the hill to the fine house. "I'll pick you up when you're finished," Daddy James offered.

"We can walk home," Mama Belle said.

Lillie nodded her head in agreement.

Mama Belle and Lillie walked onto a broad veranda that stretched around three sides of the sprawling house. The wide veranda gave an air of sheltered repose, unlike the lofty pillars of the last plantation where they had worked. They knocked on the front door. After a moment, Mrs. Noble opened it. "Come in," she invited. "The two of you look like scared rabbits. Come in. Sure hope you amount to more than my last housekeeper."

"We work our best," Mama Belle promised.

Lillie stared down the massive hall to the sweeping flight of stairs leading to the chambers above. On the left, a door led into a library. Mrs. Noble led them straight through the hall to the dining room. Chandeliers hung above the glistening tile floor. A fire crackled in the fireplace. Mrs. Noble showed them the details of cleaning the big room. Lillie gazed around the elegant room. "You can dust the furniture while your daughter shines the silver," Mrs. Noble said.

"Yes, ma'am." Mama Belle curtsied.

Lillie followed Mrs. Noble over to the sideboard where the silver was laid out ready to polish. "I want this shining like new," Mrs. Noble said.

Lillie bobbed her head. She quickly learned to shine the silver that Mrs. Noble used for entertaining. She picked up the pieces one by one and rubbed them till they gleamed. She dreamed of the day she would have rich things like Mrs. Noble.

With Christmas approaching, Lillie longed for Pappaw and Mammaw. "Daddy James, Mama Belle?" she asked one day. "Can we spend Christmas with Pappaw and Mammaw? I miss 'em so much."

"Well," Mama Belle said, "your grandma sent a message the other day inviting us. Would you children like that?"

Lillie nodded her head dramatically. Tucker and Walker agreed. Lillie twirled ecstatically around the shabby room, singing at the top of her lungs. She couldn't wait to spend time with their grandparents again in their old home.

chapter seven

An Orange for Christmas

Daddy James pulled the wagon in front of their shack. "Come on, tomorrow be Christmas, and we need ta go get us a Christmas tree ta celebrate." The family piled into the wagon, and off they rode to the woods. After selecting a small evergreen tree that would fit in their tiny shack, Daddy James and Tucker sawed and sawed with a cross-cut saw until it fell over. They all helped push it onto the wagon, and the horses trotted toward home.

Mama Belle popped some of their precious popcorn, and the children helped her string the white kernels to decorate their tree. Before they went to bed, the three children each hung their old stockings on the wall, hoping something would be in them by morning.

On Christmas morning the children bounded out of bed. Lillie followed her brothers to the living room, tingling with anticipation. *Would there be anything in her stocking?* Lillie took her stocking off the hook. It was heavy and bulged at the bottom. She carefully dumped it onto her hand. "Oh, an orange!" Lillie cried. She caressed the round fruit. Closing her eyes, she put it to her nose. "It smells so good." Even though there were no gifts under the tree, the children were delighted with their fruit.

Daddy James and Mama Belle watched the excited children. "I'm glad we get to celebrate this Christmas as a family," Daddy James said. "It's a gift jes' to be together."

"When I talked to Mister Big Ike's Sue in town befo'e we moved, she told me she's jealous of our family," Lillie said wonderingly. "I always thought she had ev'rything a girl could ever want."

"Poor Sue," Daddy James said. "Wealth and high station have made her a lonely girl. Maybe we should do somethin' for her."

"Yes, let's," Lillie exclaimed, her cheeks pink with excitement. "She tol' me she loved ta hear us sing. Could we go ta her door and sing for her?"

Daddy James shook his head doubtfully. "I'm 'fraid they won't let us in, but we could try. Let's try stoppin' there on the way to Pappaw's tomorrow."

The next morning, Daddy James loaded the family in the wagon, laid his guitar under the seat, and headed to the nearby plantation. Daddy James pulled up to the front door, and they all climbed out, smoothed their cotton clothes, and tiptoed up the grand stairway. Daddy James rang the doorbell. *Clang, clang, clang!* It rang through the quiet morning.

The door opened a crack. "James, what are you doing here? Change your mind about working for me?" Mister Big Ike opened the door and stepped outside.

Daddy James shook his head. "No, it's nothin' like that. Lillie would like ta sing a Christmas carol for your daughter Sue."

Mister Big Ike frowned. "I don't allow niggers inside my front door, James. You should know that. Go around back to the kitchen door."

Daddy James bowed submissively. "We sure will. Could you please tell Sue we be here?"

Mister Big Ike's eyes narrowed. "I don't encourage my daughter to be friends with the likes of yours." With that, he turned and slammed the front door. The children heard the bolt turning in the lock.

"Don' listen to his words," Daddy James told his family. "Mister Big Ike never did have any respect."

The children followed Daddy James to the back of the house. The servants gladly opened the door and let them inside. "We're gonna sing you a Christmas carol," Daddy James said. He propped his guitar on his knee and started strumming.

"Silent night, holy night, all is calm, all is bright," the family sang together.

The black people gathered around and clapped and swayed. "Amen, thank ya, Lawd," they cried.

Lillie glimpsed Sue peeking through the kitchen door. She sang louder. Sue smiled at Lillie.

They finished their song. "Merry Christmas!" the servants cried.

"Merry Christmas!" the Johnsons chorused. Lillie lingered, hoping to get another glimpse of Sue. All at once, the little white girl burst out of the house. "Lillie!" Sue cried. "I'm sorry my father was so rude. I like you even if he doesn't."

"No matter," Lillie said quietly.

"And thank you for that beautiful song." Sue touched her hand. "Sorry, I need to go before they find me." She disappeared around the corner of the house.

Lillie ran around the house to catch up with her family. "Why can't Mister Ike be kind to us like Sue?" she asked.

Mama Belle took her hand. "We can't feel hard toward Mister Ike. The hate in his heart goes deep. We gotta love people even when they wrong us." Her gaze focused somewhere in the distance. Slowly she patted Lillie's small hand with her rough one. "We gotta love 'em," she said softly.

Climbing onto the waiting wagon, they headed to Pappaw and Mammaw's house. Mr. Noble had given Daddy James a whole week off for Christmas, and they were anticipating a wonderful time with their grandparents and cousins.

Lillie leaped off the wagon as soon as it stopped. "Mammaw," she cried, bursting through the front door. "We're home!"

Mammaw pulled her into a hug. "Home?" she asked. "Don't you live in a better place now?"

Lillie shook her head. "No, Mammaw, our shack is tiny. Wind whistles through the cracks, and at night, I can even see the stars through the roof."

"Oh, my," Mammaw said. "What do you do when it rains?"

"We move the beds to the middle of the rooms where there aren't any holes in the ceiling. Daddy James says he will patch it soon."

"I surely hope so," Mammaw said. "You're welcome to stay here as long as you want."

Daddy James's eyes twinkled. "We might wear out our welcome."

Mammaw shook her head. "Never! I miss y'all so much." She gave Lillie another hug.

Lillie gazed in awe at the kitchen counter and table groaning with the load of food. "Mammaw?" She looked at the kitchen filled with good things to eat. "Did ya cook all month?"

Mammaw laughed. "No, Lillie, we all worked hard this week. Aunt Bernice helped me get ready for today. I want you ta jes' eat ta your heart's content." Mammaw squeezed Lillie close. "I missed you, Lillie."

Lillie ate. She ate till she was stuffed—collard greens, cornbread, lima beans, turnip greens, pork with all the fat, stuffing, string beans, beets, sweet potato pie, egg custard, white potato pie, blackberry cobbler, coconut pie, chocolate cake, jelly cake. Family and neighbors came from everywhere. Lillie's cousin Nora came too, from the other side of Canton. Lillie couldn't remember meeting her before.

"Hi, Nora," Lillie said shyly.

Nora sniffed in disinterest. "I had ta come. My mama made me."

"Do ya wanna play?"

"I'm too old ta play."

"Should we walk down to the creek?" Lillie asked, trying to find something in common.

"I guess." Silently she trudged beside Lillie.

"I'll show ya my favorite places," Lillie offered. Lillie showed her the fallen log where they had caught the turtle, the special place where her Daddy James caught fish with a net, and the wide spot in the creek where Tucker, Walker, and Lillie would go swimming in the hot summer.

"We don't ever have time for fishin' and swimmin'," Nora said.

"Don't have time?" Lillie asked. "What do ya do when you aren't workin'?"

"My daddy doesn't work. He's lazy." Nora spit out the words.

"Oh." Lillie was sober. In her heart she was thankful her daddy worked.

When they got back, the house overflowed with even more relatives. Lillie and Nora each picked up a tin plate. "Do you like sweet potato pie?" Lillie asked.

Nora wrinkled her nose. "That sounds like poor people's food. I prefer pumpkin."

Lillie blinked. Poor? Food covered the table. *How could they be poor?* She quietly filled her plate and found a place to sit all alone.

The wonderful day at Pappaw and Mammaw's came to an end, and one by one, families loaded up their wagons and headed for home.

"Mammaw?" Lillie snuggled up to Mammaw after the cousins were gone and they were alone. "Nora didn't wanna play with me."

Mammaw folded her to her ample bosom. "Don't worry, Love. Nora has lots of hurts in her life. She takes it out on those around her. I saw you trying real hard to be kind. That's a good girl."

As the new year of 1933 dawned, the Johnson family returned to their drafty shack, bringing Mammaw with them. She would be staying with them for a time. One morning, as the children stumbled sleepily into the kitchen, they saw Daddy James standing with a peculiar smile on his face. "You have a little brother," he told them. "His name is James."

Lillie tiptoed into Mama Belle's bedroom. A dark curly head lay nestled in her mother's arms. Mama Belle opened her eyes. "Come see him, Lillie. He's beautiful." Mama Belle laid the baby in Lillie's arms.

"He's so tiny!" Lillie exclaimed. "Look at his itty bitty fingers."

The baby puckered up his lips and whimpered. Lillie rocked him back and forth. "Awright, Jamie," she crooned. "It's awright."

As Jamie grew, he became Lillie's special charge. He didn't want to let Lillie out of his sight. He cried every time she left him.

"Oh, awright," she would say as she swooped him up and put him on her hip. "What's your problem anyway, Jamie?"

Jamie would nestle closer, and Lillie would pat his curly hair. His thumb would pop in his mouth and soon his eyelids drooped and he was fast asleep. Lillie would lay him on Mama Belle's bed and tiptoe away. Lillie felt very important, being responsible for her little brother. Now that Jamie was the baby of the family, maybe she would be treated like a grownup.

chapter eight

White-Hooded Visitors in the Night

One night in early spring, the Johnsons were all in bed, tired from their long day of work. Lillie woke with a start. "James! James, don't let them take you!" Mama Belle was screaming.

Lillie bolted out of bed and ran with her brothers to the other room to see what was wrong. Six white-hooded men stood in the doorway. "You are James, I assume," one man said.

Daddy James nodded.

"We have come to punish you for your crime."

"Crime?" Mama Belle screamed again. "He did nothin' wrong."

"Oh, yes, he did," one hooded man sneered. "We know he was flirting with a white woman in town."

Eight-year-old Lillie shivered, remembering the tales she had heard of horrible crimes committed by the Ku Klux Klan. Blacks weren't allowed a fair trial, and many were hanged for crimes they had never committed. What would happen to Daddy James?

"No, he didn't," Mama Belle cried desperately. "He be an honest man.

He always been faithful."

They hooted with laughter. "He did nothing wrong, she says." Their guns clicked with authority.

Lillie stood woodenly, clutching Tucker's hand, as she watched them force her Daddy James's hands behind his back and tie them tightly with rope. "Daddy James," she whispered, "I love you."

Her Daddy James looked at her briefly with a haunted look. "I didn' do nothing wrong," he said softly.

"I know you didn', Daddy James," Lillie whispered back.

Mama Belle fell on her knees in front of the men. "Please, don' take my husband." Tears dripped on her clasped hands.

The hooded men shoved Mama Belle aside and grabbed Daddy James. Poking a gun between his shoulders, they shoved him out the door. Lillie's heart beat fast as she watched her Daddy James stumble down the road, the road that would take him away from them.

Mama Belle pulled Lillie in her arms as she sobbed, "Oh, Lillie, I can't even think 'bout what they'll do to my James."

"What will they do, Mama Belle?"

Mama Belle shuddered. "I don' even want you ta know, it's that horrible." But Lillie remembered hearing her daddy talk with Uncle George about the horrible things authorities forced black jail inmates to do. They forced them to work in coal mines, and often they died in those dangerous, damp places. Sometimes they hired out the inmates to plantation owners so the authorities could make money from their labor. But tonight, Lillie knew her daddy wasn't an inmate. They hadn't come to force him to do any work. They had come to lynch her daddy. He would swing by his neck from a rope tied to a tree branch high enough that he couldn't touch the ground with his feet, and he would die a horrible death. His body would hang there as an example to others. He would be eaten by vultures, and no grave marker would even bear his name.

Lillie huddled close to Mama Belle. "Please pray, Mama Belle!" she pled.

"Oh, Lawd Jesus," Mama Belle rocked on her knees, "hear my prayer."

"Oh, yes," Lillie chanted.

"Save my dear James from these wicked men."

"Save my Daddy James," Lillie cried.

Mama Belle prayed long into the night. The children curled up beside her on the hard floor to wait. None of them slept except Jamie, who somehow had stayed asleep through the whole ordeal.

As the sun broke over the fields, Mama Belle roused herself. Moving slowly as if she had aged overnight, she stirred the coals in the cook stove, coaxing them to life and adding wood to the fire. She melted some lard in a pan and fried some bacon with eggs, but no one was hungry, and no one ate. All they could think of was, "Where is Daddy James?"

Mama Belle's haunted eyes stared at her children. "We need ta work today whether we feel like it or not. We can't slack off and spend our time cryin' over Daddy James. He would want us to work hard like we always do." Her voice sounded dull and hoarse after praying all night.

Lillie knew she wouldn't be able to stop thinking about her Daddy James, but she took the milk bucket and turned to leave. "Lillie, take me, take me," Jamie cried.

"No, you stay here. Mama Belle needs you," Lillie told the little boy.

Jamie's eyes looked sad, but he didn't cry. He curled up on Mama Belle's lap.

Lillie squared her shoulders as she and Walker trudged the mile down to the river bottoms where they kept their cows. She sat down on the stool and began cleaning the cow's udder. Walker took a bucket and grasped the teats on another cow.

Squirt, squirt, squirt, the milk sprayed into their pails.

Neither one spoke. Sadness hung over them like dense fog.

Finally, Lillie could stand it no more. "Walker, do you really think they'll hang Daddy James for somethin' he never did?"

Walker shrugged. Then he spat out, "Why wouldn't they? They don't like us niggers none." He said no more, but Lillie could see his face muscles working as he tried to control his emotions. She knew he was just as afraid as she was, but tried to be brave for her sake.

The buckets filled slowly. Lillie didn't care today; she felt no motivation to do anything. Nothing mattered except that Daddy James was gone.

They finished the milking, picked up their frothy milk buckets, and started the long walk home. As they neared the house they heard shouts. Was Mama Belle screaming again? Lillie strained her ears, then they both broke into a half walk, half run. The milk sloshed over the edges, but they didn't care. They rushed to the door and burst inside. "Daddy James!" they shouted. Dropping her pail, Lillie threw herself into his arms. "You're back again."

Daddy James's mouth showed a brief half smile, and he held her out to look at her face. "It's me. And am I glad ta be home!"

Mama Belle laughed and threw her arms around them both. "I'm frying you up a slap good breakfast." She put some more bacon and eggs into the sizzling pan.

"Lillie, get some fresh milk," Mama Belle ordered. "Pour some for all of us."

Lillie got the tin cups down from the shelf and poured each person a cupful.

Mama Belle set the platter of breakfast on the table, and everyone sat down. Eggs and bacon were dished out, and they all forked the food into their mouths with gusto.

"How did you 'scape?" Walker asked.

Daddy James's face tensed. "I was never so scared in all my life. I stumbled along in front of those men all the way ta where the mob had gathered. They were gonna lynch a whole group of blacks. I knew I had done nothin' wrong, but I knew they would never believe me. When I was close to the group, the Klan asked, 'Was this man involved with you?' The black men all shouted, 'No, James was not with us.' The men asked again, but they kept sayin' the same thing. They sat me down beside a tree, and they kept quizzing the group of negroes. Finally, they came over and cut my rope from off my wrists. 'We're sure you are guilty, but we can't prove it, so we are letting you go.' I couldn't believe my ears. I didn' wait 'round in case they might change their minds. I lit out of there in a hurry."

Mama Belle hugged Daddy James again. "It be a miracle! I prayed all night God would keep you safe. It be a miracle, I say!"

Daddy James put his arm around his wife's shoulders. "Call it what ya want, but the fact is, I'm here again."

"A miracle," Mama Belle said firmly. "I prayed, and God answered my prayer."

The next morning, Lillie walked with Mama Belle to Mr. Noble's plantation house on the hill. They cleaned and polished, swept and mopped. As Lillie dusted the furniture in the sitting room, her eyes fell on a newspaper lying on the side table. "Banner County Times," she read. She scanned the front page. The headline screamed at her:

FIVE LOCAL BLACK MEN GUILTY OF FLIRTING WITH WHITE WOMAN

Some of the words in the short article were too hard for her to read, but she understood this much; five men had been accused of flirting with a white woman and the Ku Klux Klan lynched them during the night. A picture of the hanging at the bottom of the page made Lillie shiver. Her Daddy James could have been one of them. She quickly hid the paper under the table so Mama Belle wouldn't see it or read it. Mama Belle had been upset enough when Daddy James was hauled off and she thought she would never see him again. She needed no reminders to further upset her.

chapter nine

What Lillie Overheard

Time moved on as the Johnson family lived on Mr. Noble's farm. He treated them well and paid them fair wages. Lillie thought they might stay there forever.

Lillie wondered if anyone realized it was her thirteenth birthday. Her family didn't celebrate birthdays, so she wasn't surprised when the day passed and no one even mentioned it.

"Belle," Lillie heard Daddy James say late that night after she had crawled into bed, "I wonder how long there'll be work here in the South for us blacks. Machines have taken over much of the hand labor. I want a better life for my family. Mebbe I should head north an' look for a better job." Lillie slipped out of her bed and crouched by the door so she could listen.

"Oh, James, we can work harder so we can make our loan payments," Mama Belle said. "And we've never had a nicer man to work for than Mr. Noble. We been here goin' on six years now."

"Even though Mr. Noble treats us good, we'll never make enough to get our debt paid," Daddy James insisted. "Sharecroppin' jes' keeps us in debt so we can't get ahead. There are better jobs up north. My relatives have lived in Clearmill, Pennsylvania, for years. I could live with my sister Florence till I earned enough ta bring the rest of you. She's offered to help me."

"I'd hate to split up the family." Lillie could hear the anxiety in her mother's voice.

"I know," Daddy James said, "but, Belle, I'd send for you and the children jes' as soon as I could pay for your trip. Eventually we'd all be together up north. I know you don' want me ta go, but would ya please think about it?"

"You're right, I don' want you ta go," Mama Belle declared. "The children are happy here."

"But there is no future in the South!" Daddy James insisted. "More and more machines are doin' our work on the plantations. They soon won't need us. I'm 'fraid someday we'll wake up and they'll throw us off this land, and then what'll we do? We'll have no jobs at all."

"James, do ya really think so?" Mama Belle asked.

"It's comin' quicker than we think. Lots of black neighbors are talkin' 'bout migrating north. And I'd like ta be settled in the North too, very soon. I could travel as a hobo an' catch rides on the rails all the way up there an' it wouldn't cost us anything."

"But James . . ." Lillie heard fear in her Mama Belle's voice. "It's so dangerous. One slip of the foot an' you'd be run over by the train. You might get shot, or you could break a leg an' be a cripple for the rest of your life." Mama Belle was getting wound up now. "Besides, it's a cold ride. An' you know how railroad workers hate hobos. You'd be arrested if they found you."

Lillie heard her Daddy James sigh. "It is dangerous, I know. I promise I won't go right away, but someday I will." Lillie heard chairs scraping across the wooden floor and knew the discussion was over. She jumped up and slipped away before her parents could discover her hiding place.

Lillie hurried to her bed and slid under her blanket. She tossed and turned as she thought about her Daddy James going north. If he did, would they ever see him again?

chapter ten

Daddy James
Finds a Way

All Lillie could think about was her parents' discussion the night before. Mama Belle had gone alone to the plantation that morning, leaving Lillie behind to clean their little shack. As she opened the door to the kitchen, she heard voices. Daddy James was talking to someone. Quietly, she closed the door most of the way, but left it open a crack so she could hear the conversation in the next room.

"I hopped the freight train in Canton," the voice began. "I found a closed boxcar so the railroad bulls wouldn't throw me off. Middle of winter too! Mercy, that was a cold ride. 'Bout froze, I did. They don't take kindly to the likes of us."

"But you still think it's the way ta go north?"

"Indeed it is," the voice answered. "There isn't any other way we can afford it."

"What were your biggest troubles?" Lillie heard her daddy ask.

"Food," the voice replied. "It seemed we were always searchin' for food. I looked for hobo jungles as soon as I jumped off a train. Could usually find 'em outside town near the railroad tracks and near a stream or river. I could always count on gettin' hot boiled coffee and mulligan stew."

Lillie had heard of hobo jungles where the travelers lived together and shared their food. She figured mulligan stew was like the stew they often had at home, especially when times were extra hard. Mama Belle used her kettle to cook the mixture of potatoes, onions, and whatever bits of meat they had to flavor the broth. Most hobos didn't carry kettles; they most likely used discarded tin cans to cook their stew over an open fire. She had seen hobos camping along the river bottoms, and suspected the occasional chicken that came up missing ended up in one of those stews.

"We'd wash our set of clothes in the river so we could be clean for job-huntin' in town the next day," the voice continued. "When I couldn't find a jungle, I had to beg."

"Beg?"

"I'd stop at a farm and ask if I could have some potatoes and carrots in exchange for doin' a little work. Some took my offer and some jes' gave me food. But many days there was no food. And one time I caught pneumonia. Thought I was gonna die, I did, but nope. Here I am safe and sound."

"How did you know where they would give a nigger a meal?" Daddy James grinned wryly. "I'm sure not all places took kindly to feedin' colored folks."

"You got that right. Hobos have their own code to live by. One, be a gen'leman at all times. Two, always try ta find work. Three, help your fellow hobos. That third rule is how we survived. Your hobo friends ahead of you are always markin' fence posts or gateposts with important information 'bout folks livin' nearby. Even if you can't read words, you can read them pictures, and they tell you if this place will give you food or what kind of treatment you can expect."

"How can I learn them symbols?" Daddy James asked.

Lillie heard a rustle of paper. "Here," the voice said. "Put these in your mind, and you'll survive."

Daddy James chuckled. "I haven't decided that I'm going yet. I gotta convince my wife."

"Hoboin' ain't for the faint of heart. People get injured 'n killed along the way. I was drug a half mile one day 'cuz I missed my step. But a buddy helped me climb on board, and I was none worse for the wear."

"What else do I need ta know?"

"Don't go at it alone. Hoboin' is respectable. We ain't like tramps that take 'vantage of everyone they meet. We got us a code to live by."

"I gotta do somethin'," Daddy James said soberly. "Our family got no money to pay our way north. I don' know how else to do it but hobo my way."

The man's voice was low. "Don' let nobody hear me say this, but I would just sneak off one day. Your woman'll never let ya go any other way."

"I'll think 'bout it," Daddy James said.

"I better scoot along," the other voice said. "I gotta big day tomorrow."

Lillie heard chairs scraping across the floor as Daddy James followed the voice outside. She peeked through the door. The paper was still lying on the table. She grabbed it and scanned it quickly.[1]

Kindhearted Lady	Kind Woman	Woman	Housewife feeds for chores	Sit Down Feed	Food for work
Food for working	Talk religion get food	Bread	Good For a Handout	Gentleman	Wealthy
18 I Ate	Alright (OK)	Easy mark	Tell Pitiful Story	Work Available	Tell a Hard luck story here
Fake illness here	Anything Goes	Sleep in barn	Can sleep in barn	Good Chance to get money here	Here is the place
Help if sick	Doctor	Telephone	Poor Man	Bad tempered owner	Dishonest Man

Lillie's heart grew sick when she thought about her Daddy James using these symbols to survive while hoboing his way north. She put the paper back on the table. She didn't want to see more. She didn't want to think of her daddy leaving.

All day Lillie went through the motions of cleaning their shack, but she couldn't stop thinking of the conversation she had overheard that morning. Her heart felt leaden every time she remembered that she carried a secret Mama Belle didn't know.

The rest of that week, Lillie could tell that Daddy James was getting restless. One day she got up the courage to talk to him. "Daddy James, you gonna be a hobo?"

Daddy James's head jerked around, eyes wide. "Lillie, how do you know anythin' 'bout that?"

Lillie hung her head. "I heard you talkin' with that man the other day, and I seen how restless you're gettin'."

Daddy James glanced over his shoulder, then put his finger to his lip. "Let's keep this our secret, all right? Your Mama Belle don' need more to worry 'bout, and I don' want her knowin' that I'm gonna leave soon."

Lillie nodded uncomfortably. "I wish you wouldn't go, Daddy James."

Daddy James pulled her tight. "Me too. But it's the only way for our family ta get a new start on life."

The next morning Daddy James was gone. Lillie wasn't surprised that he sneaked off during the night without telling Mama Belle. Part of her felt excited at the thought of him seeing new places and different people. But deep inside, she was scared too. Most of the life she had ever known was right here on a few square miles of sharecropped cotton land. What if Daddy James didn't find what he was looking for? Would he even be able to come back? Lillie pressed her hand over her pounding heart. *How long will it be before I see my daddy again?*

Mama Belle wiped her eyes and squared her shoulders. "Daddy James's gone." She took a deep breath and firmed up her chin. "He's goin' north to find us a place to live. We gotta keep workin' here until he sends for us."

"Will Mr. Noble let us keep livin' on his farm?" Tucker asked. His deep voice sounded like Daddy James's.

Mama Belle's jaw dropped. "Well, I sure never thought of that. I guess we'll stay here till he tells us to move on. I wonder if James told Mr. Noble he was gonna leave."

A month went by. Then two months. Then three. They heard nothing from Daddy James. Mama Belle kept working for Mrs. Noble. She worked harder than ever, grimly determined to never let on to the children that she felt sorry for herself.

One evening she invited some poor ragged children to come home with her.

"Lillie," she said, "get these poor babies somethin' to eat."

Lillie cut some squares of cornbread and spread them with molasses. She passed them out to the dirty children who sat politely on a bench in the front room. "Here ya go," she said, offering each of them a piece.

"Thank ya," they said before stuffing their mouths with the delicious treat.

Mama Belle knelt in front of them. "Would ya like me ta tell ya a story 'bout a little boy who shared his lunch with Jesus?"

The black heads nodded. "Yes, ma'am."

"When Jesus lived on earth, He was kind to everyone. Soon many people followed him. One day, Jesus' twelve disciples asked him, 'Master, these people be hungry. How we ever gonna feed 'em all?' Jesus asked them how much food they had. 'Only one small boy has five loaves an' two small fishes,' they says. Jesus knew there were more than five thousand people to feed with one lunch!"

"That much food would never feed all them people, ma'am," one little boy offered.

"You're right, son. But Jesus can do the imposs'ble. He took that little boy's lunch, blessed it, an' told His disciples to pass out bread to all them people."

"I bet some of them people never got no food," a black-eyed girl said with hard-earned wisdom.

Mama Belle shook her head. "Nope. The Bible says everyone ate their fill, and the disciples picked up twelve baskets full of leftovers!" she concluded dramatically, rolling her big brown eyes for emphasis.

"I wish Jesus would live here," came the little girl's tiny voice. "I wouldn't never be hungry again."

Mama Belle leaned close and smiled into the pinched little face. "Jesus *is* living here!"

"Then why is I hungry?" the little girl asked solemnly.

Mama Belle pulled her close. "He don' always give us all we think we need." By now Mama Belle's face showed a glimpse of the anguish she shared with their little visitor.

"That's awright." The little girl straightened her thin shoulders in a pathetic imitation of the motion Mama Belle had done so many times. "I don' need that much food. But when my stomach rumbles it feels like it need a little somethin'."

Lillie handed her a doll. "Would you like ta play?"

The little girl's eyes sparkled. "Yes, ma'am." She hugged it tightly as she slowly swayed back and forth singing softly, smoothing the doll's hair with her grubby little hands.

"Let's sing," Mama Belle said, and in her beautiful voice, she sang,

> I love to tell the story of unseen things above,
> Of Jesus and His glory, of Jesus an' His love.
> I love ta tell the story, b'cause I know 'tis true;
> It satisfies my longin's as nothin' else can do.
> I love ta tell the story, 'twill be my theme in glory,
> Ta tell the old, old story, of Jesus an' His love.[2]

The children clapped to the music. Mama Belle sang song after song about Jesus loving children.

"Them poor little ones," Mama Belle said after they left. "They don't know nothin' 'bout Jesus. We need ta keep tellin' them stories an' show them the way ta God."

"It helps me not miss Daddy James so much when I'm helpin' them," Lillie said quietly. She blinked hard and turned briskly to her work.

One morning not long after, a knock sounded at their door. When Mama Belle opened it, Mr. Noble stood there. "Mrs. Johnson?" He nervously fingered the cigar he held in his hand. "Have you heard anything at all from James?"

Mama Belle shook her head. "Nothin'."

"I was disappointed when he left so suddenly. I never had such a good chauffeur before. I know it's been hard for you with him gone. I hate to put more on you, Belle, but without James to work for me, I need to ask you to move off my land."

"I understand," Mama Belle said. "You've been mos' kind ta our fam'ly durin' our years here. We be movin' right away."

"Thank you, ma'am," he said, tipping his hat. "I'm sorry I have to do this."

Lillie watched Mama Belle square her shoulders again. "We'll soon be joinin' James in the North. Then we won't have ta depend on someone else ta provide for us. I'll ask my parents if we can move in with them while we wait."

The next day the remaining Johnson family returned unannounced to the same plantation they had worked on most of their lives. "Lillie, you're getting so big. It's good ta have ya back again!" Pappaw said when they arrived. He enfolded her in one of his giant bear hugs.

Lillie laughed. "I like living with you too, Pappaw."

Still they heard nothing from Daddy James. Five months. Six months. Seven months.

One morning Lillie walked out with Mama Belle to the mailbox at the end of the lane. There was a letter with a postmark from Clearmill, Pennsylvania. Mama Belle's eyes shone as she hurried to the house to open it.

> Dear Belle,
>
> I'm sending enough money for tickets for you and Lillie and Jamie to get to Chicago. I want you to stay there until you are able to travel again. I will send your next train tickets to Aunt Chloe in Chicago.
>
> I'm sorry I can't afford to bring the boys yet. I will need to save money for their trip later. We will all be together again soon. I miss all of you.
>
> All my love,
>
> James

Mama Belle looked sadly at her boys, who had listened eagerly to Daddy James's letter. "Boys," her voice trembled a bit, "be brave. Daddy James said to stay here until you are able to join us in the North. It won't be long, I promise."

Tucker put his arm protectively around Walker. "We'll be fine. Pappaw an' Mammaw will take care of us until we can leave. After all, I'm almost seventeen."

The next day Lillie walked with Mama Belle to Canton. They needed to use Daddy James's money to purchase some things for their long trip to Pennsylvania. "What can I get you today, Auntie?" the shopkeeper asked when they stepped inside the door.

Mama Belle smiled at the honor shown. Auntie was a term of respect used to address older black women. Her quiet dignity showed in the graceful set of her neck. "I need some new shoes for my daughter, please."

Lillie's feet tickled as the young man put her foot on a metal gauge and measured what size she would need. He brought out five pairs. "Try these," he said, offering her a stool and kneeling in front of her. "How do they feel?"

Lillie wiggled her toes. The shoes felt hard and tight. She knew she would have to wear them a while before they limbered up. "They's mebbe too tight," she said uncertainly. She tried on another, and then a third pair. Finally, she found one pair that felt good on her feet.

Proudly she wore the shoes home.

"You gonna wear those shoes out before we even get started," Mama Belle said. But Lillie could hear the smile in her voice. She felt the excitement in the air. Finally they were heading north! At last they were going to see Daddy James again.

chapter eleven

The Long Train Ride

The next morning, Pappaw, Mammaw, and Lillie's brothers took Mama Belle, Lillie, and Jamie to the train station. Jamie clung to Lillie and buried his face in her shoulder as the shiny black train puffed, spewed smoke and cinders, and rumbled to a stop.

The kind black porter directed Mama Belle to the Jim Crow car for the colored people. Lillie had heard about these cars. She scowled and planted her feet rebelliously on the ground. Weren't she and Mama Belle just as good as those white ladies holding their pretty new skirts out of the dirt as they stepped daintily into the first class cars? *We be the ones who iron those frills of yours, my fine ladies,* Lillie thought angrily. *Why do ya think that makes us like the dirt you's steppin' on?*

The black porter guarding the first class train car narrowed his eyes at Lillie and shook his head slightly as if to say, *Jes' wait; our time's a'comin'.* Mama Belle hissed at her and tugged on her arm, glancing in alarm at the white family beginning to board. Lillie gave in and reluctantly turned away from the Whites Only car. *Pappaw always tol' me God made me jes' the same as the white girl on the hill, but it sure don't look like any of them figgered that out yet.* Pappaw and Mammaw followed them to the door. Mama Belle hugged her parents, then held her boys tightly before climbing the steps.

Lillie saw Walker bravely swipe at his eyes with his hand. His cheek glistened with tears. "I'll miss you both," he whispered as he hugged Lillie and Jamie. Lillie saw his face crumple as he quickly turned away.

Lillie handed Jamie up to Mama Belle, then turned and clung first to Mammaw then Pappaw. "You mus' go, my little Lillie," Pappaw said, pulling her arms away from his neck. "Goodbye, little one," his said, his lips brushing her hair. Lillie quickly hugged her brothers, and Pappaw lifted her aboard.

"We'll take good care of 'em," the porter promised.

Lillie followed Mama Belle and Jamie down the aisle until they found a seat. They crammed their suitcases around their feet since there were no luggage racks like in the white people's car. The dark faces around her made Lillie feel at home, but the hard vinyl seats were plain and uncomfortable. Lillie wiggled and squirmed trying to find a comfortable spot, and they hadn't even started off yet. She gazed out the window, scanning the platform. She waved to Pappaw, Mammaw, and her brothers. They waved back, and Mammaw wiped her eyes.

The train puffed and groaned as it started. Faster and faster the wheels rolled until it felt like they were flying. Lillie's eyes stung and her heart hurt as she watched the station disappear from sight. She would miss her brothers, even though she knew she would see them again soon. But what about Pappaw and Mammaw? Would she ever see them again?

Mama Belle laid her head back to rest. It seemed Mama had been extra tired recently. Jamie held tightly to Lillie's hand as his big brown eyes stared out the window. The train sped down the track toward Chicago, where they would stay with their Aunt Chloe and Uncle Emmet until Daddy James sent them the train tickets to Clearmill, Pennsylvania.

The black porter soon came by their seat. "Headin' north?" he asked.

Mama Belle smiled she handed him their tickets. "Yes, we be on our way to a better life. My husband sent the tickets for us to come north." Her voice showed her thankfulness.

The porter winked at Lillie. "Seems everyone is headed that way. I wish you the best." He handed the punched tickets back to Mama Belle. "If there's anythin' you need for you or your children, jes' ask me."

"Thank you," Mama Belle said. Snuggling a thin blanket around Jamie, she told Lillie, "Go ahead an' rest, now. You ben workin' hard these past days. Get you some rest."

The swaying of the train soon put Lillie to sleep. She dreamed about the city she would find at the end of her trip. *Only one drinkin' fountain,* she realized drowsily, half awake. *Black an' white folks usin' the same one. Sharin' the sidewalk, an' the black folks don' hafta step off in the gutter. They's all the same.* She awoke with a start when the train stopped at the next station to load more passengers. Lillie sat without moving for a few moments, thinking about the city she had seen in her dream. *I wonder,* she thought, *if any of that will be real? Or will the North jes' be the same for black folks? Pappaw always said, "Someday—black folks will be equal with white." I wonder if "Someday" be here yet. Or if I'll ever see it.* After the train left the station, Lillie felt a little braver. "Can I walk 'round a bit?" she asked Mama Belle.

"Yes, but don' get outta my sight," Mama Belle said, pressing a hand to her stomach as a look of pain crossed her face.

"What's wrong, Mama Belle?" Lillie asked with concern.

"Jes' a little pain." Mama Belle caught her breath and forced a smile. "It's better. Go now."

Lillie walked all the way to the front of the car. A big sign hung over the door to the next car. "Whites only," it said. Lillie didn't dare open the door, but she stood on her tiptoes and looked in the window at a beautiful dining car, decorated in gold and green. Long rows of tables were set with silverware and pretty napkins. Rich white people sat sipping wine, waiting for their food. Waiters with bow ties and black aprons hurried back and forth serving the white people anything they wanted. *Someday, maybe in Pennsylvania,* she thought, *I am gonna have such a life. And I'm gonna be respected not only by the blacks, but by the whites too.*

Daddy James's sister, Chloe, and her husband, Emmet, stood waiting on the platform when the train rumbled into the Chicago station. "Belle," Chloe gushed. "You have such a beautiful family."

Lillie gaped at her aunt, taking in every detail of her fancy clothes. Her ebony skin gleamed, and her black eyes sparkled. *She looks like a fine lady,* Lillie thought. Uncle Emmet stood by her side, tall and dignified in a gray suit and fedora hat.

After the family settled in the wagon, Uncle Emmet took the reins and clucked to the horse. Lillie plugged her ears. The city noises made her ears hurt. She wasn't sure she liked this city.

Lillie stared down the street they were traveling. Dilapidated boarding houses with rickety steps that connected the three stories lined the street. "Do you live here, Aunt Chloe?" Lillie's voice was apprehensive.

"Thank God, no," Chloe said. "We were able ta buy our house long before all the black people rushed up here. The city isn't buildin' more housing, so the blacks comin' from the South don't have any place to go except here in the Black Ghetto. The owners even divided small apartments in half so they could put twice the people in and make more money. Problem is, the tenants who live in the other halves don't have heat, light, or running water."

Lillie stared at all the black children running on the streets. She had never seen so many people crowded in one place. Five scantily-clad boys pulled a wobbly wagon piled high with bits of metal, bottles, and other junk. "What are they doing?" Lillie asked, pointing at them.

Aunt Chloe turned her head to see what Lillie was pointing at. "The city pays those boys some pocket change ta clean up trash. With so many children runnin' around, delinquency is a big problem."

Lillie frowned. "What's that big word mean?"

Aunt Chloe chuckled. "That means boys and girls not behaving. This gives them something to keep them busy."

Lillie sighed with relief when they turned the corner and drove down a quieter, tree-lined street. "Here we are," Uncle Emmet said as he jumped down and tied the reins to a post.

Mama Belle and the children climbed down. Jamie grabbed Lillie's hand as they walked up the sidewalk. "Do Aunt Chloe and Uncle Emmet live like white folks?" Lillie whispered loudly.

Mama Belle put her finger to her lips.

They walked up the front steps, waited while Aunt Chloe unlocked the door, and stepped into a grand hall. Lillie's mouth dropped open. Was it possible to be black and own so much?

"Come now," Aunt Chloe said, laughing at Lillie's surprise. "Let me show you to your room."

Lillie's head swiveled from side to side as she followed her aunt up the grand staircase to a long hall. "You and Jamie can stay in this room, and your mama will be across the hall."

Lillie's eyes widened as she looked at the tall bed, spread with a white coverlet. On the floor was a little trundle bed for Jamie. "Look, Jamie! It's so pretty." Lillie tiptoed to the bed and smoothed the white, fluffy cover.

Aunt Chloe took Lillie to the bathroom at the end of the hall. She showed her how to turn the tap to get hot or cold water. Lillie grinned, watching the clear water run into the clawfoot tub. She loved the comfortable feel of the hot water. She took the bar of fragrant soap from the side of the tub and lathered it all over her body. Now she smelled just like Aunt Chloe. She climbed out and dried herself with the soft, fluffy towel. She pulled her old nightgown over her head. She felt like a queen as she climbed into her bed. She thought she wasn't going to sleep a wink, but next thing she knew, she woke up to the sun streaming in the window.

She hurried to wash her face in the bathroom sink, remembering how Aunt Chloe had showed her to turn on the water. It was marvelous! She hoped Daddy James's house in Clearmill would be like this.

Downstairs, Mama Belle and Aunt Chloe were having tea in the dining room. Lillie stopped at the doorway when she heard them talking. "You can stay here until you feel able to travel," Aunt Chloe said.

"I don't want to be a burden," Mama Belle said.

What are they talking about? Is Mama sick? Lillie took Jamie's hand and led him into the dining room. She stared shyly at her cousins, Ralph and Marlin, already seated at the table, eating their breakfast. "Howdy-do," she mumbled as she took her place. They grinned at her, but continued filling their mouths. Aunt Chloe hurried to the kitchen and soon reappeared with fried eggs, bacon, and biscuits.

"Now, have more biscuits," Aunt Chloe encouraged. "They're my own special recipe."

Lillie thought food had never tasted so good. She ate one biscuit, then two. She eyed the platter hungrily.

Aunt Chloe passed the platter around again. "Belle, you need one too. You need ta keep your strength up."

Mama Belle sighed. "No thanks. I'm not hungry. I have a question though. What makes colored folks flock to Chicago anyhow?"

"Ever hear of the Chicago Riot?"

Mama Belle shook her head. "Can't say that I have."

Aunt Chloe cleared her throat. "In 1919, 'bout twenty years ago, a black boy drowned after swimming into the area reserved for whites near the Twenty-Ninth Street beach. That wasn't far from where we drove today. Anyhow, the policeman refused to arrest the whites who attacked the black boy. Whites and blacks threw rocks at each other, and violence jes' got worse all over. For weeks, white gangs stormed the streets of the Black Ghetto, burned houses, and fired shots. Thirty-eight people died, over five hundred were injured, and over a thousand became homeless. Many people believe the unrest encouraged the first migration. Have no idea why."[1]

"Riots destroy people in the North," Mama Belle said. "Just like lynching does in the South."

Aunt Chloe nodded. "It's all the same spirit, a hatred for colored folk."

"It don't make sense," Mama Belle said. "How can people hate that much?"

That night, Lillie lay wide awake in her bed. *Seems like black folks jes' can't get a break, no matter where they go,* she thought resentfully. *Pappaw would say we gotta love folks even when they do us wrong, but sometimes that's jes' plain hard!* She tossed in her bed, listening to the unfamiliar city sounds. A tear trickled down her cheek and plopped on her pillow "I miss you, Pappaw and Mammaw," she whispered. *Oh, well,* she mused hopefully, *maybe Clearmill won't be like Chicago. Maybe we'll be able to live like rich folks there someday.*

The next morning, Mama Belle didn't come downstairs for breakfast. "Your mama isn't feeling well," Aunt Chloe told the children when they shyly walked into the kitchen.

"Can we see her?" Lillie wanted to know.

"Not now. Why don't you take Jamie to the library? You can read whatever books you want."

Lillie took Jamie's hand and led him down the grand hall. "Mama Belle's sick?" he asked.

"Yes, Jamie, we need ta be extra quiet today so Mama Belle can get well." The two children entertained themselves all day with a bookcase of fine books.

One book especially intrigued Lillie. She couldn't begin to read all the words, but the pictures told the stories. She looked at the pictures of Jesus feeding the five thousand and remembered Mama Belle telling that story to the poor children from the river bottoms.

All the while, though, Lillie listened for Mama Belle. She heard Aunt Chloe quietly going in and out of her mama's bedroom. Soon the doorbell rang. Aunt Chloe hurried to answer it.

"Come in, Doctor," Chloe said. "She's upstairs. I'll take you to her."

Lillie watched wide-eyed as a dignified black man carrying a black valise followed Aunt Chloe down the hall and up the stairs. She heard murmurs in her mama's room above them. *What's wrong with Mama Belle? Why can't we see her?* Lillie's eyes filled with tears. Mama Belle must be very sick. Lillie didn't remember a doctor ever coming to their house in Mississippi. Instead, Pappaw always prayed over them, and they were healed. "Pappaw, where are you?" Lillie whispered. "Mama Belle needs your prayers right now." She laid her head on her arms. Weary from the activity and the worry over her Mama Belle's health, Lillie soon fell asleep.

"Lillie?" Jamie touched her arm timidly. "I's hungry."

Lillie sat up and rubbed her eyes. What time was it anyway? How long had she been sleeping? She needed to find Jamie some food. "Come, Jamie," she said as she reached out and took his hand. "There be food in the kitchen, I know. I'll find you somethin' to eat."

Lillie pulled Jamie down the hall and toward the kitchen. She pushed open the door, but stopped when she saw Aunt Chloe sitting at the table. Her beautiful kinky hair stuck straight out, and her head was in her hands. She turned as the door opened. "Oh, 'scuse me, Aunt Chloe." And Lillie stepped back and closed the door.

"Come here, child," Aunt Chloe called. "What do you need?"

"Jamie is hungry, but I didn't want to bother you none. I was gonna see if I could find some leftover biscuits from last night."

Aunt Chloe gathered Lillie and Jamie in her arms. "I forgot about you in all the goings on. You must be feelin' like you could eat an elephant.

You sit right down, and I'll fix you enough food to make your tummies pop." Lillie and Jamie scooted the bench close to the table and sat on it.

"You two have been quiet today," Aunt Chloe said as she stirred and poured and stirred some more. "Your Mama Belle will be up in no time. She had a hard time last night. And the little one died."

Lillie's eyes widened. "A baby?"

Aunt Chloe nodded. "A little girl. She lived only a short time. I called the doctor, but he couldn't do anythin' either."

Tears dripped off Lillie's nose. *A little sister? And she died?* "Poor Mama Belle. Can we see her?"

"She's sleeping now, Belle is. I'll let you see her when she wakes."

So that's why Mama Belle had seemed so tired and in pain on the train. Why couldn't the baby live? We're going to a new life with Daddy James, and the baby should go too. Lillie tried to swallow the hard lump in her throat. She could only nibble at Aunt Chloe's good biscuits and gravy. When Mama Belle woke up, Lillie and Jamie hurried to her bedside. Mama Belle held them close and stroked their hair. "Little Kate is with the Lawd," she told them. "Poor baby took only a few breaths. She was a pretty one, she was. But God declared she was too good to live on this earth. Bless the Lawd. She never has to live poorly or dress in rags."

Lillie sniffled. "But Mama Belle, Daddy James never even saw her."

"I know." Mama Belle wiped her own tears. "But we can't be bawlin' our eyes out for what wasn't to be. Daddy James will send for us soon now, and we can all go to him in Clearmill."

Lillie swiped her eyes with her hand. She needed to be strong for Mama Belle. She wouldn't cry again.

chapter twelve

A New Home in Clearmill

Mama Belle slowly regained her strength. Aunt Chloe made the arrangements for baby Kate to be buried in a black cemetery in Chicago. When Mama Belle felt strong enough to make the trip, Aunt Chloe and Uncle Emmet loaded them up in their wagon and drove them over to see the little grave. A large oak tree stretched its branches over the small mound of dirt as if to protect it from the tangle of brambles that threatened to crowd over it. A hand-carved cross read:

Kate Powell Johnson
Infant of James and Belle Johnson
Died in childbirth

Mama Belle had no address to write and tell Daddy James that baby Kate didn't survive. She figured that by now Daddy James would have moved into their new home, but she didn't have his new address. So they waited for a letter from him. One week, two weeks, then it was a month. Finally, the postman brought a registered letter.

Dear Belle, Lillie, Jamie, and baby,

Here are the tickets for your train ride to Clearmill. I hope all is well. I can hardly wait to see all of you and of course, to meet the newest little Johnson.

Love,

James

"Poor Daddy James." Lillie smoothed the paper with her hand. "He doesn't even know."

"No mind," Mama Belle said woodenly. "He'll find out soon enough. We need to pack up and get ready for another train ride. It leaves tomorrow."

Lillie looked around the beautiful bedroom she would be leaving. She finally had a taste of what it would be like to live rich. She wondered what waited for her in Clearmill. Would they be rich like Aunt Chloe and Uncle Emmet? She loved living like this and wasn't sure she wanted to give it up.

The next morning, Aunt Chloe and Uncle Emmet took them to the station to catch their train. Uncle Emmet shook Lillie's hand and said a polite, "Goodbye."

"Take care of your Mama, now," Aunt Chloe told Lillie. "She's going to need to rest. I'm going to miss you." She hugged Lillie and Jamie.

"Me too, Aunt Chloe," Lillie said.

Climbing aboard, the children found their seats. Exhausted, Mama Belle immediately fell asleep. "Let's go explorin'," Lillie said as she took Jamie by the hand. They tiptoed past Mama and crept to the end of the car. A sign above the door to the next car read, "Whites Only."

"Do we dare?" Lillie looked down at her brother. Jamie nodded. Glancing around, Lillie cracked open the door. Jamie clung to his sister's hand as they stole into the next car.

"Hey, you, nigger girl!" a white porter snarled. "Get back into your car. That's the only place for the likes of you."

Terrified, Lillie turned and ran to the train door and pushed it open. Pulling Jamie through, she slammed the door and hurried to their seat. Mama Belle opened her eye. "You young'ns behavin' yourselves?" she asked.

"We jest went explorin'." Lillie hung her head. "Sorry," she murmured. Jamie snuggled close to his sister, and soon his sleepy head rested on her shoulder. Lillie's cheeks burned. She hated being treated as inferior just because she was black.

After another long trip, the train lurched to a stop at the Clearmill station. Lillie scanned the wooden platform for Daddy James, but she couldn't pick him out of the sea of people. How would it be to see Daddy again?

Mama Belle gathered their things. "Lillie, you carry this trunk, and I'll get the rest. Jamie, you follow Lillie. Hold on ta her dress so you don' get lost." They walked to the end of the car and stepped down. Lillie didn't dare look away from Jamie and Mama Belle as they jostled with the moving crowd on the platform.

Suddenly Lillie heard a familiar voice call above the noise of the crowd. "Belle, Lillie, over here!"

Lillie saw a man waving at the end of the platform. Her heart leaped. It was Daddy James! He zigzagged his way through the crowd. "You're here! I've been waitin' all day." Daddy James first scooped Lillie up in a big hug, then Jamie. Then he enfolded Mama Belle in a loving embrace. "Belle?" He held her out at arm's length and looked her up and down with a perplexed frown. "Where's the baby?"

"S–she didn't make it, James," Mama Belle's voice cracked and tears sprang to her eyes. "We buried her in Chicago."

Daddy James swallowed hard. "You did? Why, Belle. Oh, I knew I shouldn't have left you alone."

Mama Belle laid her hand on his arm. "There was naught you could've done. She wasn't meant ta live on this earth. Chloe even called the doctor, an' there was naught he could do either."

Daddy James shook his head, bewildered. "I just can't believe it."

"It's true. She was a pretty little thing. We named her Kate." Mama Belle laid her head on her husband's shoulder for a moment. "But let's not linger, James. The rest of us are here, so let's be thankful. Now, let's go home."

Daddy James tried to smile as he looked at each one of them in turn. "My blessings finally got here."

"Daddy James," Lillie asked, "do you have a rich home like Aunt Chloe and Uncle Emmet?"

Daddy James smiled. "I'm 'fraid not, Darlin'. But I've worked hard since I came those long months ago." He turned to Mama Belle. "You don't need much to be happy, do you?"

Mama Belle shook her head. "Only bein' with you."

Daddy James pulled her close again, then helped her onto the waiting wagon. He said no more until they were all settled and swaying down the road. "It's been hard startin' over," he began. "Jobs are hard to find. Look at that sign over there."

Lillie looked at the handwritten sign posted on the street corner. Scrawled on it were the words:

NO JOBS FOR NIGGERS UNTIL EVERY WHITE MAN HAS A JOB

Across the street another sign boldly declared:

NIGGERS, BACK TO THE COTTON FIELDS —CITY JOBS ARE FOR WHITE FOLKS

Lillie's heart sank. Maybe black people wouldn't have a chance here either. She had thought it would be better in the North. *Why are we hated everywhere we go? Why can't we have the same chance as everyone else?* she thought bitterly.

Lillie pushed away her thoughts and stared at the big factory buildings along the streets. Clearmill bustled with industry, but she didn't plug her ears this time. Although the streets weren't as busy as Chicago, she would need to get used to living in a strange, new town.

When they arrived at the house on Park Avenue, Lillie studied the stately white house. It wasn't as tumbledown as their shack in Mississippi, but it looked older than Aunt Chloe and Uncle Emmet's. She helped Daddy James carry their bags inside. Worn carpets lay across the creaky floorboards. Lillie looked up at the tall ceilings and big windows. Heavy drapes swooped aside with a sash, and faded floral paper spread across the walls. The place was charming in its own way, lots better than their shack in Mississippi, but secretly Lillie had been hoping for a fancy house like Aunt Chloe's in Chicago.

"I had Aunt Florence fix us some tea and cookies," Daddy James said, speaking of his older sister who had moved to Clearmill years ago. "Let's sit down. We have some catching up to do."

Lillie sat and slowly nibbled her cookie. "Want 'nother one," Jamie said, his mouth full of crumbs. Lillie reached for another one and gave it to Jamie while she listened to her parents talk.

"Belle," Daddy James sighed, "hoboing wore me out. It took me weeks to get here. One of my buddies fell off the train an' got run over. We had ta leave him lying there 'cause we couldn't get off the fast-movin' train." Daddy James shivered.

"I stayed well an' strong. Got chased by angry dogs more than once, but a little treat always tamed 'em. I was glad ta get here and so fortunate ta find a place to live before all the places were snatched up by other colored people movin' north."

"Oh, James," Mama Belle said. "I worried 'bout how your trip went. I prayed for ya every day. Did ya know Mr. Noble made us move off the farm after ya left?"

"I was afraid he would," Daddy James sighed. "I didn't tell him I was leavin', hopin' he would feel sorry for ya and let ya stay. Where did ya go?"

"We moved back in with Pappaw and Mammaw. They gladly gave us a home. But it wasn't the same without ya. We were so happy when ya sent for us."

"Well, I'm just glad you're here. Now ta get the boys here next, an' we'll all be together. It's not gonna be easy startin' over, but stayin' in the South woulda been worse."

"You might be right, James," Mama Belle said.

But the Johnsons would soon find that life in the North posed a different set of challenges for them and the other blacks who were streaming northward. As southerners, they were unprepared for the harsh winter weather and the difficulty in finding a job. In the South, blacks had all the hard physical labor they wanted, but in the North, even whites were willing to do hard labor. Competition was fierce, and creativity and a business mind were necessary to succeed. But these were two things their heritage of slavery had not taught the blacks. Slavery had simply taught them to work hard and do what they were told. In addition, many blacks were unable to read and write. But the Johnsons knew how to read, and this would help them get better jobs than most of the blacks coming north.

When Lillie woke up the next morning, she poked her head out the window. Instead of fields of fluffy white cotton, corn, or peanuts, she saw streets. Cars sped past their house. Lillie felt a twinge of sadness. It just wasn't the same as her old home. Would she ever love this town like she loved her home on the plantation?

A black woman hurried her child down the street, and two black men strolled by. Daddy James had told her how white people had once lived in this neighborhood, but they had all moved away when the blacks started to arrive. Lillie tried to imagine high society women passing by with their feather hats many years ago. The white people's houses they had passed farther downtown were much more modern than the houses in this neighborhood.

Lillie pulled her head back in and gazed around her bedroom. "I finally have wallpaper like Sue's," she said to herself. "But now it doesn't seem important. All those flowers on paper never did anything to make Sue happy."

Lillie remembered what Mammaw would often tell her, "Life is more than just strivin' to be rich, Lillie. It's 'bout makin' the best out of the life God give you." Just maybe she was starting to understand what her grandmother meant.

Aunt Florence had a hotel several blocks away, and during the day Mama Belle would sometimes help fix beds and fold towels. Daddy James had found a job just down the street at Humphrey Cleaners. Lillie walked importantly down the street with him that morning. It was the first of many days that she helped Daddy James at his job. She shook rugs, laundered clothes, and pressed suits. She never got paid, but she liked helping her daddy get his work done so he could spend more time with them in the evenings. He always had more work than he could accomplish, even though he worked hard. Daddy James put in many extra hours to keep customers happy.

One day a woman opened the door, dragging in a big area rug. "I would like this rug cleaned," she told Daddy James.

"It'll be a couple weeks 'fore I can get it done," Daddy James said calmly. "I'm booked all week long."

The woman's face grew red, and the veins in her neck bulged. "Y–you nigger," she hissed. "You will have this done this week, or I will report you to the police."

Daddy James didn't flinch. "I'll do it soon as I can." He wrote down her name and phone number and laid her rug on the pile of waiting rugs. Lillie's breath came jerkily, her eyes blinked rapidly, and she waited to see what terrible thing was going to happen next. *Are white folks always gonna be mean to my Daddy James, no matter where we live?*

The woman slammed the door behind her as she walked out. "Some people just don't like us much," Daddy James said, shaking his head, "but the law says we got our rights just the same. I ain't budgin'. She can wait same as anyone."

Lillie looked up at Daddy James, admiring his bravery in standing up to a white lady. Maybe there was hope for the future after all here in the North!

When Daddy James called the lady the following week, Lillie expected another outburst. Lillie could hear her heart pounding in her ears as the bell on the front door rang. The lady's heels clicked as she walked to the counter. "How much do I owe you?" the lady asked calmly.

"Fifty cents," Daddy told her.

She quietly counted out her coins. Lillie watched from the window as Daddy James helped the woman carry her rug out to her waiting car.

Daddy James brought home his monthly pay. He proudly handed the cash to Mama Belle. "You're the one with the business mind," he said.

Mama Belle carefully counted out the cash and gave Daddy James $2 for the cigarettes he had recently started smoking. "I asked down at the corner store, James, and they said you can buy a carton of ten packs of those cigarettes for $1.20. That saves a nickel compared to buying the two packs for 25¢. You make sure you do that, now," Mama instructed. She set aside a stack of cash to pay bills, figuring carefully to herself and counting it twice. Then a certain amount to buy groceries. The rest she handed to Lillie with a sigh of relief. "Put it in the can."

Lillie reached on her tiptoes to pull the tin can down from the top of the icebox. She dumped out the wad of bills, added the new stash, and then counted the money for her brothers' tickets. It wasn't enough yet.

Finally, after six months of hard work, Daddy James had saved the $65 to bring Tucker and Walker from Mississippi. On the day they were to arrive, Lillie and Daddy James went to pick them up at the train station. Lillie's heart sped up as the train rumbled to a stop. Her feet danced with impatience on the wooden planks. It had been so long since she had seen her brothers! She pulled her coat tighter as a chilly wind blew through the station. Down the line of cars, she saw Tucker and Walker step down from the train and make their way across the platform.

Daddy James slapped them on the back affectionately. "You boys got big," he declared, looking them over.

Lillie felt shy in front of her two burly brothers. Tucker reached down and grabbed her before she could get away. "I missed you," he said as he rubbed her cheek with his chin.

Walker slapped her shoulder. She smiled up at him as they walked to the wagon. "We missed you too," Lillie said. "Did you know Mama Belle had a baby in Chicago on our way up here, and she died?"

Startled, the boys looked at Daddy James and he nodded. "It's true, boys. We didn't let you know. She was buried in Chicago. Your Mama Belle named her Kate." The boys nodded in stunned silence. They had learned at a young age to meekly accept life's hard knocks.

As the wagon rattled down the street, Lillie sat back contentedly between her two brothers. It was so nice to be together as a family again. If only Pappaw and Mammaw could be with them. *But at least we have Uncle Percy and Aunt Florence in the neighborhood. It'll be different not to spend Christmas with Pappaw and Mammaw, but at least we have someone nearby to call family.*

chapter thirteen

A White Christmas and a Tall, Dark Stranger

L illie pulled the soft white coverlet tightly over the guest bed and fluffed the goose-down pillows like Aunt Florence had shown her. Now fifteen years old, she had started helping at her aunt's hotel next door. Baby Annette had joined the family, and Mama Belle stayed home now to take care of her.

"Will we ever live like the rich?" she asked Daddy James that night as she gladly counted out her earnings and put them in Daddy James's hand.

"We be rich, Lillie." He playfully cuffed her shoulder. "Rich in family and love."

Lillie was quiet. *Maybe being rich is more than money,* she thought. She watched Daddy James drop the money she earned into the tin can on top of the icebox. She knew they needed every possible penny to make ends meet. *I guess we won't be getting any gifts this year for Christmas,* Lillie thought wistfully.

It snowed that Christmas Eve, 1940. The Johnson children crowded around the living room window for their first real look at snow. They watched in amazement as the white flakes floated from the sky. "Can we eat them?" Jamie asked.

Lillie giggled. "You can try. It's frozen water."

As the snow drifted down outside, Walker and Tucker pulled out a checkerboard and Lillie played Blindman's Bluff with Jamie. Even Daddy James joined in the fun for a while, tying a scarf across his eyes and chasing Jamie and Lillie around the wide living room. Mama Belle came from the kitchen carrying cups of steaming eggnog. As Lillie sipped its deliciousness, she looked happily around the room at her family. Last Christmas Eve, they had sat around the fireplace in the shack as Pappaw read the Christmas story. How she missed Mammaw and Pappaw! *But I'm so glad Daddy James is with us this year. And tomorrow we'll get to eat at Aunt Florence's hotel, just like rich people.*

Aunt Florence closed her hotel for the holidays but made a gourmet meal for her family—wild goose with cranberry sauce, boiled potatoes, collards, and chiffon cake for dessert. "Oh, Auntie," Lillie said, filling her mouth. "I've never had such grand food. Makes me feel rich." Her eyes shone with delight.

Aunt Florence laughed. "We are rich, chile. Rich in family, food, and friends. We ain't needin' any other riches."

Lillie glanced at Daddy James. That is just what he had told her the day before.

Mama Belle helped Aunt Florence clean up the dining room while the children played outside. Tucker, Walker, and Lillie helped Jamie build his first snowman. Jamie patted and rolled, and soon his ball was so heavy he couldn't lift it. "Walker, can you lift this ball?" he asked his big brother.

Walker hefted the snowball onto the larger one sitting on the ground. "One more ball for the head," he said. "This time make it smaller."

Jamie licked his glove. "It just tastes like water." His voice showed his disappointment. He had thought it would taste like the white sugar it resembled!

They rolled the last ball together, and Walker lifted it on top to finish the snowman. From the coalbin, they found small lumps of coal for his eyes, nose, and mouth. The snowman smiled at them as they stamped their shoes on the porch before going back into the hotel. All too soon, it was time for the Johnsons to go home.

The white coat of winter was left behind and spring flowers pushed through the cold ground. Lillie couldn't wait for spring. This cold weather took some getting used to.

Beside Aunt Florence's hotel was the Market House, fondly called "the heart of Clearmill." As soon as the weather grew warmer, local farmers brought eggs, milk, produce, and many other things to sell. Automobiles parked all around the building. The booths under the roof bustled with activity. Lillie loved to walk through it on her way home from work.

"Hey, nigger girl," a vendor called one day. "Get out of here."

Lillie bit her lip and slunk into the shadows. She wasn't going to let that vendor deter her from doing her shopping. Mama Belle had asked her to buy some eggs and milk before she came home, and she was not leaving the market without them. She hurried to the next stall. "Hello, ma'am," she said politely. "I need a quart of milk and a dozen eggs for my mama."

The lady behind the counter looked over her glasses at the black girl in front of her. "Here you are. That'll be forty-five cents."

Lillie counted out the coins and handed them to the lady. The vendor shoved the food toward Lillie without looking at her and quickly turned her back. The milk had slopped over the edge of the bottle and hadn't been wiped off. One of the eggs still had chicken manure on it. Lillie hesitated, but knew she must swallow her irritation, or something worse might happen. She quietly said, "Thank you, ma'am," and hurried on, her face burning. She wanted to get out of there before she was yelled at again. She knew blacks and whites both shopped at the Market House, but that didn't stop the white vendors from insulting the blacks.

Lillie didn't bother telling Mama Belle about her experience in the Market House. It was all too common, not worth bringing up to the family. They all experienced similar insults every day. *We jes' gotta love folks.* Once again she rehearsed Pappaw's admonition. *We jes' gotta keep on lovin', even when they do us wrong.*

Lillie carried the plates to the supper table. "How did your day go, Tucker?" Her big brother helped himself to generous portions of the steaming food.

"I'm a foreman now." His voice showed his satisfaction. "They just promoted me. There's even some white men working under me!" The family's surprised congratulations chorused around the table. Tucker freely informed them of the details of his work at Channelock Tool Factory. "Heating that steel is mighty tricky. If we heat it too much, it will be too brittle, and the tools will snap when they're used. If it's not heated enough, the tool will be soft and won't have the strength it needs."

Walker added, "They're calling Clearmill 'Tool City' because we have more tool shops than any other city this size in the United States." He reached for another biscuit. Nodding at Tucker, he said, "We were mighty lucky to get good jobs. Most of the blacks coming up from the South can hardly find work, unless they want to be servants or janitors. I guess that's better than what we had before, but not much." Walker still harbored some bitterness.

Tucker wasn't to enjoy his foreman position for long. Lillie entered the house to fix lunch one day and found him sitting at the table, staring at a paper in his hand.

"What's that?" she peered curiously over his shoulder.

Silence met her query. "Tucker! What's going on?" Lillie shook his arm.

"Oh! Lillie. You're here," Tucker said absently.

Lillie frowned impatiently. "Well, yes, Tucker. I *am* here. I asked what you have in your hand." Her sarcasm went unnoticed.

Tucker heaved a sigh that came from his toes. He cleared his throat nervously. He tried to speak but couldn't seem to find the words. Finally he just handed the official notice to his sister. "I'm eighteen now. I guess I should have expected this."

It was a notice to report for military service. The United States had entered World War II, and Tucker had been drafted to serve in the army.

When Mama Belle heard the news, she clutched baby Annette to her as if to protect one of her children, at least. Daddy James just kept patting Tucker on the back, shaking his head and saying nothing. Walker barely kept from bursting out with questions, trying to respect his parents' distress. Jamie looked from one to another, bewildered, aware that something was amiss but not sure what it was. Lillie didn't know how to feel. She buried her face in her brother's shoulder and clung tightly. Their home was joining the ranks of many families in America separated by the war.

Lillie missed Tucker and worried about his safety. One day she ran home from the post office with one of the few letters they received from him. She could hardly keep still while she waited for the rest of the family to come. "Hurry, Daddy James! It's a letter from Tucker!" she hollered out the door.

"All right, we're all here now. You're our best reader, Lillie. You go ahead." Daddy James sat heavily at the table and blew out a hard breath. He braced his gnarled hands on the table and prepared to receive whatever news the letter contained.

Tucker never told much about the war. It was as if he wanted to protect the ones at home from the ugliness of jungle warfare. " 'Devastation is everywhere,' " Lillie read now. " 'We are starving from lack of food and water.' " Her voice faltered. Mama Belle moaned softly. Lillie cleared her throat and continued. " 'Today we went to a stream to get a drink. I tried to remember how hard our life was in the South, but somehow it didn't help when I saw bodies . . .' " She stopped, horrified.

"Go on." Daddy James's voice was husky.

"Okay, Daddy," Lillie whispered shakily. " '. . . bodies floating in the same stream where we got our water.' " Lillie shivered. Even though she tried to be thick-skinned, she had a hard time getting that mental picture out of her mind.

Lillie struggled to adapt to her new school in the North. Her only friends were her family. She spent long hours alone reading, studying, or working after school hours. At school, girls tried to draw her in. "Lillie, come play with us," they coaxed.

Lillie shank back in her corner. She shook her head. She always felt awkward in public, so she became quiet and withdrawn. But that was before she met Percy Lee.

In her senior year of 1943, Lillie studied extra hard. She wanted the best grades she could make. As a result, she spent even more time alone. She had almost no friends except Percy Lee.

"Come on, Lillie, let's go ta the Y this afternoon after school," Percy said one day as they gathered their books at the end of their school day. The YMCA, part of a nationwide move to provide African Americans with structure and social life, offered many programs such as swimming lessons, sports, and after-school activities.

"I dunno," Lillie said doubtfully. "I have so much homework."

"Homework, bonework," her girlfriend scoffed. "You can do your old schoolwork later. I wanna swim."

Still Lillie hesitated. "All right," she finally conceded.

They grabbed their bathing suits and headed for the Y. Many of their friends from school were there too. After changing in the shower room, they raced to dive into the pool. For the next half hour, they splashed and swam laps. Lillie enjoyed herself more than she wanted to admit. "Did ya notice that cute new boy at school this year?" Percy Lee whispered to Lillie.

Lillie shook her head and rolled her eyes. "No," she said. "I'm too busy tryin' to get good grades."

"You need ta have more fun," Percy Lee declared. "Come with me ta the ice cream parlor after we are finished. You can meet him."

I'm not interested in boys, Lillie thought, but she said nothing. She finished quickly, wrapped a towel around herself, and hurried to the shower room. She didn't wait for Percy Lee. She wanted to be out of there as quickly as she could. *I'll never be noticed by boys anyway.* But as she walked down the street, she saw ahead the ice cream parlor that served blacks. "Seale-Lily Ice Cream," the sign read. The slogan under it said, "You eat it with a smile." Why not wait for Percy Lee and her gang? Lillie quietly walked into the parlor, hoping to find a secluded seat. She picked a stool all the way at the end of the counter.

"Hello," the young man behind the counter greeted her. "What can I get for ya today?"

"I'm waitin' to meet some friends, but I'll take a root beer float, please."

"Certainly," the young man said. He hurried away and was soon back with her treat. She paid him and waited.

Soon she heard Percy Lee, giggling and talking as she entered the ice cream parlor. "Lillie," she gushed. "I thought you went home. Come here, Leo," she motioned to a tall black boy by the door. "I want you ta meet my friend."

Lillie politely answered his questions, but stayed as uninvolved as possible. She soon slipped out of the ice cream shop and headed home to study.

Three years later in February of 1946, Lillie headed out the door for a Friday evening youth social at the Methodist church. Her freshly pressed wool skirt rustled and a smart-looking sweater completed her outfit. Mrs. Brown, a Christian white lady, planned a social every week for the under-privileged black young people. Lillie strode down the sidewalk toward the church fellowship hall. "I don't want to be late," she murmured to herself. "It's the bright spot in my week."

Percy met her at the door. "Oh, Lillie, did ya hear about the boys just discharged from the war?" she bubbled.

Discharged? She hadn't heard anything from her brother Tucker. She hoped he would soon be home too. Surely he wasn't injured or dead. Lillie bit her lip, and a slight frown creased her brow.

"Lillie?" Percy Lee asked again.

"Oh," Lillie said, startled. "No, I hadn't heard." She knew about army boys. Most of them were handsome but uninterested in loners like herself. She sat in the corner observing while her popular friend mingled with the boys.

She listened as one boy spoke. "I enlisted in the army 'cause I loved my country. I believed in helpin' America become the greatest nation in the world."

Lillie recalled Winston Churchill's pronouncement the previous year. "America at this moment," the British prime minister had said, "stands at the summit of the world."[1]

But the returned soldier was still speaking. "I soon found out that blacks are just as segregated in the army as at home. Most of us Negroes had ta work in warehouses or do other humble work while the white boys had the sought-after jobs. We spent our evenin's pickin' up trash while the white soldiers relaxed in the segregated USO club, dancing and watching movies. Life was unfair in the army too."

"Oh, that's terrible," Percy Lee said. "You would think you'd be accepted if you are workin' for the same cause."

"You would think so, but that's not the way it was. When we returned from one assignment overseas, a white crowd yelled at us and stripped off our uniforms at the railway station."

"What! Why did they do that?" Percy Lee asked, astounded and angry.

"No matter how much we gave to this country, it's still a white country, and we're jes' blacks. We won't change that. Sometimes I wonder why I even fought for the privilege to be only half American."

Lillie watched the boy as he talked. His handsome face looked kind, but troubled. He glanced her direction, but she quickly looked away. Why was her heart beating so fast?

She needed something to do. She hurried over to the pool table and picked up a cue stick. The young man followed, "Mind if I join you?" he asked easily.

Lillie blushed. "N–no," she stuttered. What was wrong with her anyway? She glanced around, hoping Percy Lee would come to her rescue, but she was standing close to a handsome army officer, making every effort to charm him.

Lillie turned back to the table. The young man picked up his cue stick and tried it for size. "Wanna break it up?" he asked, looking at the fifteen balls in a triangle.

Lillie shook her head. "Go ahead." Her voice trembled.

He laughed. "All right, here goes." He lined up his stick with the cue ball and took aim. He smoothly made the break, and the striped ball rolled into the pocket at the other end. Lillie knew now she was going for the solid-colored balls. "Your turn!" he said after making another perfect shot.

Lillie blushed again. She was usually good at pool, but tonight she felt rattled. Time after time her aim was off, and in the end, he won the game with little competition from her.

He held out his hand. "We haven't introduced ourselves yet. I'm Edward

Clark. What's your name?"

Trembling, Lillie touched his hand in a quick shake. "I'm Lillie Johnson."

"I've never met you before. Are you new to the youth socials?"

Lillie shook her head. "No, I come often."

"I guess I've been away too long. I don't remember seein' you before. I hope you aren't afraid of me," he said softly.

"No, I don't think I am."

"Wanna try another round?" he asked. "I bet you're good at this game."

"I—I don't think so. I seem to have lost my touch!" Lillie laughed nervously. She quickly laid her cue stick on the pool table and turned to leave, wiping her palms furtively on her skirt.

Instantly, he was beside her. "Let me get you some punch," he offered.

Before she could say no, he guided her to the table and dipped and filled a cup for her and one for himself. He took a sip. "Tell me about yourself."

Lillie relaxed as she told him about living in the South as a child, moving to the North as a teenager, and now learning to live where blacks were a minority. "The job we know best is slavery. And as a result, we often find jobs of the same nature."

Edward's eyes were full of understanding as she talked. He seemed to feel her struggle, and she felt compelled to tell him more. "I have always wished for somethin' more, but now I wonder if my dreams will ever be fulfilled."

Too soon, the chaperones announced it was time for the party to break up. "Will you . . . be here again next week?" Edward asked timidly as they walked out the door together.

"I wouldn't miss it," Lillie said.

"Then I'll be here too." He turned and walked down the street in the opposite direction.

chapter fourteen

Wishes and a New Beginning

That night, Lillie lay in bed and rehearsed the events of the evening. Was she beginning to love Edward? She needed to get a hold of herself. She was a private person; how could she have blurted out so much of her life story to a stranger? But as she thought about her conversation with Edward, he didn't seem like a stranger.

The next morning, Lillie heard a deep voice in the kitchen. She bounded out of bed and hurried down the stairs. "Tucker!" she cried. "Are you trying to give us all a heart attack, or what?"

Tucker smiled, but Lillie thought his eyes looked sad. "We had to sneak home from the train station durin' the night. We were afraid of hateful reactions from people who never wanted to be involved in this war in the first place."

"It's so unfair," Walker chimed in.

"It is," Tucker sighed. "But the truth is, war makes people react in all kinds of crazy ways."

"Well," Lillie said, "you're still our hero."

Tucker smiled again but said nothing. The following days Lillie noticed Tucker seemed quiet and withdrawn.

"The war's done somethin' to him," she heard Mama Belle say quietly to Daddy James one night in the kitchen.

"He's seen sights no young boy should ever have to see," Daddy James replied. "It's made him lose his carefree outlook on life."

"I'm just thankful he found a job again at the tool factory. Most veterans aren't that fortunate to get the job they left before they went off to war," Mamma Belle said.

Edward fought in the war too, Lillie thought. *What terrible sights has he seen?*

The next week at the youth social, Lillie watched the church door anxiously. Would Edward come again as he had promised? Sure enough, the door opened, and he stepped inside. Scanning the faces, Edward walked straight to Lillie. "May I sit beside you?"

Lillie nodded.

The activity of the evening was "Spin the Bottle." The first spin pointed toward Lillie. She uncorked the bottle and pulled out a question. "If you could make two wishes, what would they be?" Lillie fingered the paper for a few minutes. "First, I would wish to have lots of money; and second, I would wish to live like a white person."

She spun the bottle, and it pointed beside her toward Edward. He pulled out the next question. "What is something special about someone in this group?" Edward looked directly at Lillie. "Lillie is a very good pool player. She has a lovely smile, and I would like to learn to know her better."

Lillie blushed and lowered her eyes. She could almost feel Percy Lee's smug grin.

Question after question taken out of the bottle kept the evening interesting. When Edward drew a slip of paper asking him to tell one thing about his family, he said that he had an autistic sister. *No wonder he is so caring,* Lillie thought. She felt her admiration rise even higher.

Edward became a regular visitor in the Johnson home. "I like you, Lillie," Edward told her one evening. "Can I call you my girl?"

Lillie's mouth fell open. "You're serious, aren't you?"

Edward's face shone. "Never been more serious in my life."

Lillie blushed. "Then I accept," she said sincerely.

Since Tucker and Edward had both fought in World War II, they had a lot in common. They spent hours talking, and sometimes Lillie crept off to bed before they finished.

One evening, Annette crawled up on Edward's lap. "Tell me a story," she said.

Edward put his arm around her. "The only stories I can think of right now were from when I served in the Pacific Islands during the war. But I'd rather forget about the whole war."

Tucker looked up from the newspaper he was reading. "I would too," he grunted.

"I want a story," Annette insisted.

Edward sat stroking Annette's kinky hair. "One day, our squadron was on a mission to check on what was left after the armies had ravaged through a certain village. I found a little girl who was jes' about your age. She was the only survivor in the whole village. I heard cryin' and found her huddled in a pile of rubble. I will never forget her big brown eyes. Her name was Huong, which in English means 'pink rose.' I couldn't hurt her. I picked her up and carried her away to hide her. She soon sobbed herself to sleep as I held her close to my heart."

"What happened to her?" Annette asked, her brown eyes wide.

Edward's strong finger traced her face. "I wish I knew."

Annette looked up into his face. "Why didn't you bring her home with you?"

"I wanted to, but I couldn't, for her safety and mine. I took her to an

American general who promised he would find a home for her in America. I hugged her tightly before I left. Her brown eyes followed me all the way out of the general's house. I'll never know where she ended up. I hope she found a happy place."

Annette studied her swinging feet. "What would it be like to have no family?"

"It wouldn't be fun." Edward's tight voice reflected his building tension at the memory. "She was such a sweet little one. She didn't deserve losin' her entire family."

Lillie's heart melted at Edward's story. She loved the way he seemed at home with her family. As the months went by, Lillie she realized that yes, she did indeed love this tender-hearted young man.

One Friday night, Edward walked Lillie home from the social. "I heard you say at that social a few months ago that one of your wishes is to have lots of money. I would ask you to marry me, but I can't promise you'll be rich."

"Oh, Edward, if we can be together, I'm sure we'll be happy."

"But I want you to think about it. Army men like me are havin' hard times finding jobs. We have no money, and our parents have no capital to begin any kind of business. I hope it will be different someday."

"It will be, Ed," Lillie said.

"I don't even have enough to give you a church wedding, Lillie. I can't ask you to give up every girl's dream."

"Silly, 'course you can. We're not gonna have no church wedding. We got no money for the likes of that. We're goin' to the Justice of Peace. He'll marry us up jes' the same, and my parents will be happy they don't have to worry about payin' for a big wedding party they can't afford."

Edward beamed with happiness. "Did I just hear you say you will marry me?"

Lillie grabbed his hand and twirled around him. "Yes, you heard right.

Now let's get goin'. What are we waitin' for?"

Without even consulting their parents, the couple decided to be married. Edward came to Lillie's home one day when she was there alone. "Ready to go?" he asked as he helped her with her coat.

Lillie handed Edward her small valise. "I'm ready," she said, her eyes sparkling. Her borrowed white dress shone brightly against her black skin.

"You're beautiful, Lillie." Edward helped her out of his car in front of the Clearmill courthouse.

The brick courthouse loomed grand and imposing. Lillie's eyes followed the tall gray columns on either side of the stairway leading to the front entrance. Her heart beat faster as Edward led her up the steps. Edward opened the door, and together they walked in and found the Justice of Peace sitting behind his desk. "What can I do for this fine-looking couple?" the justice asked as he took off his reading glasses.

"We would like to be married, sir," Edward said.

"And you realize the vows you will be taking? Vows for life?" The justice's eyes peered at them.

They nodded.

"Wait here while I get my ceremonial robes." The justice hurried out and soon returned wearing a flowing black gown and carrying a book. Standing in front of them, he opened the book and cleared his throat.

"Now, what are your names?" He looked at Edward.

"My name is Edward Clark."

The justice turned to Lillie. "And your name, Miss?"

"I'm Lillie Johnson."

The Justice of Peace cleared his throat again. "We have gathered here today with Edward Clark and Lillie Johnson to share in the joy of their wedding."

Edward took Lillie's hand in his.

The justice continued. "Marriage is a path of life, given by God, so that the husband and wife may provide each other with companionship, help, comfort, joy, and, most of all, love. Love is patient and kind; love is not jealous or boastful; love is not arrogant or rude; love does not insist on its own way; love does not rejoice at wrong, but rejoices with the right. Love bears all things, believes all things, hopes all things, endures all things. Love never fails.[1] Edward and Lillie, we rejoice with you now as we witness your vows to love each other. And now, do you, Edward, take Lillie as your wedded wife, promising to tenderly care for her, to respect her, to cherish her, and to faithfully love her until death?"

Something came and went across Edward's face, so briefly Lillie wasn't sure she saw anything. His head jerked as if brushing away an irritating insect, then his white teeth shone in a toothy grin. He looked down at Lillie. "I do," he pronounced, chest puffed out confidently.

The justice turned to Lillie. "Do you, Lillie, take Edward to be your wedded husband, promising to tenderly care for him, to respect him, to cherish him, and to faithfully love him until death?"

"I do," Lillie said, blushing.

"And now you will enter the greatest journey of your life. In as much as you have agreed to enter the marriage relationship, it is now my honor and privilege to pronounce you husband and wife. You may now kiss the bride."

Edward leaned over and tenderly kissed Lillie.

"And now," the justice said, "let's get your marriage certificate written out for you."

His robes flapping, the Justice of Peace stepped over to his desk. He laid his robes aside and pulled a paper from a file drawer. Across the top it read, "Certificate of Marriage." He wrote the date: April 8, 1946, their wedding day.

Edward handed him $2, and they each signed their names on the marriage certificate. The clerk added his signature as a witness to the simple ceremony. Lillie felt almost in a dream as the Justice of Peace stamped the certificate firmly. Lillie fingered the embossed surface of the impressive-looking official seal as she picked up the certificate and handed it to her new husband.

She slipped her hand in Edward's as they walked out of the room. As soon as they were out of the courthouse and down the steps, Edward scooped Lillie up in his arms. "My beautiful bride! My family will be proud."

He carried her to the street where he had parked his little beat-up car and placed Lillie in the passenger seat. He closed the door and hopped into the driver's seat. Leaning over to give her a kiss, he said happily, "I still can't believe this! We're married! By the way, Lillie, I hope you won't mind livin' with my parents for a short time. I want to get us our own little place soon, but I need to wait until I can find fulltime work. You understand, don't you?"

Lillie gulped. "It doesn't matter, Edward, as long as I have you." But it did matter. They hadn't discussed where they would live. She didn't want Edward to know she assumed he had a place all picked out for them. A slight shadow hung over the rest of the day for Lillie. The unwelcome thought flitted through her mind, *I wonder what other disappointments marriage will hold for me?* She firmly banished the thought and determined to focus on her joy at finally having someone who belonged only to her, who would never leave her, just like he promised. She would show Edward she was happy no matter where they lived.

chapter fifteen

A Growing Family

"Lillie," her mother-in-law said crisply one morning, "I want you to dust and shine your room better than you did last week."

Lillie gulped. "Yes, ma'am," she said. She lifted her skirts and hurried back up to the rooms she and Edward shared. She attacked the dusting and polishing with vigor. Her cheeks flamed. She wouldn't let Edward be ashamed of her. If his mother noticed dust, Lillie would clean her rooms every day.

A sigh escaped Lillie's lips as the dust rag in her hands swept across the furniture. She could still hear the condescension in her mother-in-law's voice as she replayed the morning's conversation in her mind. Her mother-in-law resented her son having married into a family of lower status than the Clarks. Lillie longed for the day when she and Edward would have their own house.

When Edward came home that night, he noticed her tear-stained face. "What's wrong, Lillie?" he asked tenderly.

"Nothing!" she said.

"Why the streaks down your cheeks?" Edward traced one with his finger.

Lillie scolded herself for not washing her face before he came home. "Your mother told me to clean my room better than I did last week."

"My mother said that?" Edward asked.

Lillie nodded.

He pulled her into his arms. "Don't worry about her. She's always fussy. I hope we won't have to live here long. I'm working hard, Lillie. I'm soon going to have enough for a place of our own."

That sounded good to Lillie. Aside from spending several hours a week cleaning a few wealthy people's homes for a small income, she spent most of her time at home with Edward's mother. The strain was wearing away at her normally resilient spirit.

One morning a year after they got married, Lillie woke up dizzy and nauseated. She lay back down on her pillow and held very still. Next thing she knew, she felt like heaving. Running for the bathroom, she unloaded all the contents of her stomach into the commode.

"Lillie?" her mother-in-law called. "Is everything all right up there?"

Lillie rolled her eyes. She felt anything but right, but she bravely said, "Yes, everything is fine." But she knew she needed to get to a doctor soon. Without Edward or his parents knowing, she arranged an appointment. She walked to a nearby doctor's office the next day. He confirmed what she had guessed.

"Edward," Lillie told her husband after he returned from his railroad job one evening. "You're going to be a daddy."

Edward smiled wide. "I am?"

"As sure as I'm your wife," Lillie said.

"That makes me happy." He put his arm around her.

His parents wanted them to move out. "A family needs their own place," Edward's mother said. "Not temporary living quarters."

That evening after supper, Edward lamented to his wife. "I'm not sure I'll be able to give you the kind of place you want."

She laid her hand on his shoulder. "Your mom will be glad when I get out of here. I don't think I'm high-class enough to suit her. She'll be talkin' 'bout the way I keep house till her lips fall off."

Edward broke into laughter. "Oh, Lillie, you're so expressive."

Edward found a nice little place with big trees in a big fenced yard. He took Lillie to see it. "I love it," Lillie said. "I can see it all fixed up and pretty with fancy furniture to make it my dream place."

Edward laughed. "I don't know about the furniture. I was hopin' to save a bit more before we got our own place. We will save and someday I'll buy you some of the things you wish for, but for the moment, can you be happy as it is?"

Lillie nodded.

Lillie bubbled with happiness in their new home. She hung freshly washed curtains they brought from Edward's parents' place. She laid a big rug in the middle of the living room and positioned the old rocker comfortably on the rug. She felt settled and happy.

"Edward," Lillie said thoughtfully one evening after he came home. "I think it's time."

Edward stared. "Y–you mean you need to get to the hospital?"

Lillie grabbed her middle and gasped. "Quickly," she groaned.

Edward snatched up Lillie's bag and led her to the waiting car. He sped to the hospital, screeched to a stop at the entrance, and ran around the car to help Lillie walk into the hospital.

Two hours later, a nurse came out to talk to the nervous father waiting for news. "You have a beautiful son," she said. "Follow me. I'll take you to your wife's room."

Edward followed the nurse down the hall. She opened a door and motioned him inside. "Lillie!" he cried, staring at his pale but radiant wife resting on a pile of pillows.

Lillie smiled and held out the bundle she cradled in her arms. "He looks like his daddy. I think we should name him Edward Junior."

Edward knelt beside her bed and pulled the little blanket back to see the tiny brown face. "He's perfect," he said. "I can't imagine a baby bein' any more beautiful." But he said the same thing when Katherine joined their family two years later in 1950; Lillie knew he loved both their children.

Now they had two children and a nice home, but very little money. Even so, life seemed perfect to Lillie. She watched Edward hold the children, play with them, rock them to sleep, and sing to them. *He is such a good father,* she thought.

One night when the children were four and two, Ed said, "Lillie, let's get the children into their pajamas and head for Airway. Tonight is family night, and each car costs only fifty cents." Airway was a large outdoor theater in Clearmill, and Lillie knew he loved going there on Saturday nights. She felt privileged he wanted to do that with his family.

Lillie quickly bathed the children and put them in warm pajamas.

"Where we goin', Mama?" Eddie asked.

"Wait and see," Lillie told him. "Daddy has a surprise for you."

Edward backed the car out onto the street, and they drove away.

"Oh, goody!" Eddie clapped his hands.

"Goody," Katherine repeated.

"I love the big, big pictures," Eddie chattered.

"Pictures," Katherine echoed.

Lillie caught Ed's eye and winked at him. They drove up to the office box and paid. Carefully, Edward found an empty speaker post in the fenced lot and parked their car as close as he could. Ed and Lillie rolled down their windows so they could hear the soundtrack. At 9:00 the screen came to life.

"Daddy?" a little voice came from the back seat.

"What is it, Eddie?" Edward asked.

"Want some caramel corn," he said.

"Corn," Katherine echoed.

"Gonna spend all our family night savin's at the concession stand," Edward grumbled. Then he chuckled. "Wait till half time, and I'll take you."

Lillie squeezed his hand. "You're a good daddy," she said.

At half time, Edward took Katherine and Eddie by the hand, and they wound their way to the concession tent. From her comfortable seat in the car, Lillie watched them go. Pretty soon they were back with caramel corn, hot dogs, and a donut for Lillie.

"Yum!" The donut's powdery crumbs melted in Lillie's mouth. "How did you know this is my favorite?"

Eddie jumped up and down. "Daddy told us, Daddy told us." His eyes sparkled.

Edward smiled at Lillie over the children's heads. They all leaned against their car and waited for the children's film to play. *Sleeping Beauty,* Edward read.

Eddie and Katherine yawned. "Tired?" Lillie asked. She helped them into the car, and soon they both fell asleep, sprawled out on the back seat.

Edward and Lillie stood side by side, holding hands and enjoying the magic of the special evening. As the last song, "Let the Good Times Roll" flashed across the screen, Edward turned and whispered, "Let's go home."

"Yes," she laughed. "These little sweethearts will wake up in their beds tomorrow morning and never know what they missed."

"It's just as well," Edward said. "The endin' songs aren't geared toward children anyway."

They climbed back in the car, and Edward wove his way carefully toward the entrance and out onto the street. At home, they took the sleeping children and carried them to their beds. "Sleep well," Lillie whispered, kissing them both on their foreheads.

"Sweet dreams," Edward murmured.

Edward quietly shut the door to the children's room and followed Lillie downstairs. "I'm a lucky man," he said. "I have a wonderful wife, and a darlin' son, and beautiful daughter." He pulled Lillie toward him. "Thank you for marryin' me."

Lillie laughed, enjoying his embrace. "And you don't think I feel the same? Ed, you are wonderful. You have never disappointed me. I love you."

The next Sunday, Lillie's parents invited them over for dinner. "Just like old times," Mama Belle told Lillie on the phone. "Tucker and his wife and Walker will join us too."

Lillie smiled as she looked around their family table. Everyone was in their place with a few added since she had married Ed and left home. The menu had changed for the better too. The creamy potatoes, the tender roast, and colorful succotash made Lillie feel like she was dining in style. "Mama Belle, this is so good. Where did you learn to make all these fancy things?"

Mama Belle smiled a pleased smile. "I learn a lot when I help in the kitchen at the hotel."

Annette chimed in. "I go with Mama Belle and help her. We usually have lots of guests to serve, and Aunt Florence couldn't do it alone."

Lillie nodded. "Seems you work too hard, Mama Belle."

Mama Belle harrumphed. "Too hard? Chile, this is nothing compared to sharecroppin', now is it?"

Lillie looked at her brothers. She could see emotions flitting across their faces. "No, Mama Belle," she said. "I'm thankful you don't have to work that hard anymore."

The family discussed the booming 1950s economy as well as troubling current events.

Daddy James laid his napkin beside his empty plate and pushed his chair back. "Did you see this article in the *Clearmill Tribune* 'bout that black woman down South?" He folded the newspaper to show the article he was referring to.

The boys shook their heads. "What happened?" Tucker asked.

Daddy James cleared his throat. " 'African-American Bucks the System.' " He read the headline and handed the paper to Edward.

Lillie's ears perked up. She could feel anger threatening to rise within her. Although their country was thriving economically, they were living in an era of great conflict. The civil rights movement, which was just begin-ning, exposed the underlying divisions of the American society—supreme white and inferior black.[1]

Edward read aloud. " 'On December 1, 1955, in Montgomery, Alabama, Rosa Parks refused to obey bus driver James F. Blake's order to give up her seat in the "colored section" to a white passenger, after the whites-only sec-tion was filled. The driver called the police, and Rosa Parks was arrested.' "[2]

"Go Rosa!" Lillie cheered, raising her hand in a victory salute.

Mama Belle's brown face creased with concern. "How's this gonna end up, now? I'm 'fraid people's gonna get hurt before it's all over."

"Time for things to change, though." Walker's anger had moderated somewhat over the years. "And ya can't expect change without some pain," he added.

The afternoon passed too quickly for Lillie. Soon she and Edward gath-ered their children. "Thanks, Mama Belle." Lillie kissed her cheek. Then she turned to her daddy. "Goodbye, Daddy James." Lillie gave him a quick hug and turned to climb in the car with her waiting family. Edward guided the car out the lane and down the street toward home.

"Can't we stay with Grandpa and Grandma?" Eddie whined.

Lillie chuckled. "No, son, we need to go home now." Lillie turned to

Ed. "Thanks for takin' us today."

Ed's big smile said more than words. Lillie felt content.

Lillie paused before the department manager's door at Grapple Zipper Company. She had been cleaning toilets in the factory for a while, but she had endured enough of that. Now she was determined to get a real factory job, one like white people had. *After all,* she reasoned, trying to pump up her courage, *this is the main employer in Clearmill. Zippers are in high demand all over the world.* She stepped aside to let a woman pass. She gave herself a brisk nod of confirmation. *Grapple employs five thousand workers, and this whole town has less than nineteen thousand people. They surely need workers badly enough to hire a black woman. I'm going to give it a try.*

"I can't give you a position here," the manager told her.

"And why not?" she probed.

"You're black," he said. "Blacks don't get good jobs like this."

"I work hard," Lillie told him. "And blacks have every right in this country to have a good job."

"Well," the manager said as he rubbed his forehead. "I've been short-handed, and I have no option but to hire blacks."

"You won't be sorry," Lillie said. "We blacks work hard. We ain't lazy. We do whatever we need to do to have a job."

"Problem is, I have only men's jobs available. Jobs like operating and servicing machinery."

"I don't care. I will take any job," Lillie persisted.

The manager looked dubious but finally conceded. "Come tomorrow morning. You will be a machine operator, and I'll give you 35 cents per hour."

Lillie eyes widened. She had never made that much money at any job.

"I'll be here." Before the manager could change his mind, she jumped up and hurried home. Operating a machine had to be better than cleaning toilets. Now she had a real job, a white person's job!

Lillie's eyes shone when Ed stepped in the door that evening. "Ed, I got me a real job."

"What's that?" Ed looked dubious.

"I asked today for a job at Grapple. The boss wasn't too sure in the beginnin', but by the time I left, he told me I can be a machine operator."

"But Lillie, you know nothing about machines." Ed shook his head.

"I can learn anything I set my mind to, you wait and see."

The next day, she stepped into the entrance of the factory, walking tall and steady. She surveyed the room full of big machines, humming and clattering in production. The machine operators turned their heads in her direction and stared. "It's a nigger," a red-headed girl said, then swore. Lillie ignored her.

A man walked up to her.

"Hello, I'm Mr. Cauldwell," he said. "I just want you to know, your color will hinder this department."

Lillie's neck grew warm, but her chin tilted proudly. "I'll work hard, and by the way, I'm Lillie."

"Don't matter what your name is, you nigger." But Mr. Cauldwell wasn't the boss, and he knew everyone had to work together to get the job done. He snorted in disgust. "But since the boss hired you, I have no choice."

Lillie didn't flinch at his unkind words. "You won't be sorry, Mister."

"We'll see," he said. "Follow me." He walked down an aisle between the roaring machines.

Mr. Caudwell stopped in front of one of the big machines. Lillie started in awe at all this thundering metal. She swallowed hard and laid her hand on her stomach to still the fluttering. She listened as he pointed out each of the machines to her: the joining machine that clamps the metal teeth to rolls of cloth tape, the cleaning machine whose wire brushes scrub down the zipper's sharp edges, the waxing machine which waxes the metal so it slides flawlessly, the gapping machine which takes out teeth to make a gap where the zipper begins and ends, and the slider machine which inserts a slider into the gap where the zipper begins.[3] Lillie's mind spun trying to follow all these descriptions. She wondered how she would ever learn to tell the machines apart, much less learn to operate them.

Mr. Caudwell leered at her. "Think you can do this?"

Lillie nodded firmly.

"I'll show you how to operate the joining machine," Mr. Cauldwell said. Lillie watched as the metal teeth moved over rollers and were joined to a reel of narrow cloth. "Watch this closely," Mr. Cauldwell told her. "It's important that all the teeth are caught solidly on the cloth." Lillie watched attentively as he showed her how to inspect it. *I can do this,* she told herself in determination. By the end of the shift, she had learned how to start the machine, stop it when the metal became derailed, and change reels of fabric and spools of metal.

"You catch on fast," Mr. Cauldwell said grudgingly. "I think tomorrow you will be on your own." He carelessly dropped the words that would change Lillie's life.

Lillie learned to operate every machine at Grapple—the joiner, the cleaner, the waxer, the gapper, and the slider. She learned the workings of each machine as thoroughly as any of the men. She felt fulfilled by the fact that she had a real job. She worked hard to prove to Mr. Cauldwell that a black woman could do the work just as well as any white woman.

While Lillie worked a man's job at Grapple, Edward worked a prestigious job in the black community. As a porter for the railroad, he traveled every day between Clearmill and Erie. He was responsible to greet passengers, carry baggage, make up sleeping berths, serve food and drinks, and keep the cars tidy. When he stepped inside the house in the evening, the children would descend on him. "Tell us a train story, Daddy," they chorused.

Edward rumpled their hair with his hands. "A train story, huh? What makes you think I have a train story?"

Katherine clapped her hands. "You always do, Daddy, you always do!"

Edward chuckled. He sat down and drew Eddie on one knee and Katherine on the other. "Today, I had a pile of shoes to shine. 'Bout that tall." He indicated a mountain with his hand. "I walked through the sleepin' car, and there beside each curtained doorway sat more pairs of shoes than I had ever seen on one trip. I gathered 'em and hauled them to my berth. I sat down with my rag and tin of polish and started rubbin' an' scrubbin' 'em until they shone. I never shined so many dusty shoes in all my life. When I got them all shined, I realized I had forgotten to mark each one with a number so I could remember which berth each one came from. I thought for sure I wouldn't get tips today." Edward laughed again. "So I piled them on my arms. Jes' like this." Edward demonstrated a big pile.

The children giggled. "That's lots!" Katherine said.

"It was tall as a mountain," Edward exaggerated. "I walked down that narrow hall. I stopped at each room. 'Shined shoes,' I called loudly, and would you know it, those white men poked their heads out, grabbed their pair, and handed me a nice tip. I decided it might be better to do it that way than quietly puttin' them back beside each doorway."

"Daddy," Eddie sighed. "Your job is so 'citing."

"I tell you only the good parts, son. I don't want you to know the other parts. Now, let's see if Mama Lillie has some dinner ready for me. I'm starved." Edward didn't tell them what happened when he was lifting a young white woman's luggage on the shelf that day. A wiry man with a business suit and hat in the seat behind her had hissed, "You stop flirtin' with white women, nigger! You gonna get a rope around your neck." It wasn't just that day. It happened almost every day. Pain cut through his heart as he recalled the gossip and attacks on his character. But his children didn't need to know that. And he never wanted Lillie to find out either.

Daddy took their hands, and together they walked to the kitchen. Lillie had the table ready. "Storytime over," Edward laughed. "We're ready for a good meal."

"It's ready," Lillie said. "I gotta leave for work shortly, but I think I have time to eat before I go."

Edward and Lillie alternated shifts, so one of them was always home with the children. It didn't give them much time together, but they cherished the brief time they did have.

When Lillie came home from work that evening, Edward had chocolates waiting and had even mopped the floor. He was always doing things to please her. "I love your black," he told her.

"My what?"

His eyes twinkled. "Your black. You're a beautiful black, and I love your black."

Lillie gave him a playful shove. "You quit your teasing."

"I ain't teasing," he said. "Come, I'm off work tomorrow. Let's go to the beauty parlor and get your hair all done up. I like you all pretty-like."

So Lillie went with her husband. Edward took care of all the details, and after several hours she sported a new coiffure like she had always admired on her teachers and other high society blacks. "Now I'm high society," she said. "Now I won't be 'shamed of seeing your mother."

Ed tilted her chin and looked into her eyes. "I like you just the way you are. You hear me? If I wanted my mama, I woulda married my mama. Hear?"

Lillie's heart sang. *I hope he always thinks of me that way,* she thought.

chapter sixteen

Prejudice and Friendship

"Lillie?" Edward's kind voice broke into Lillie's thoughts after the children had been excused from the dinner table one Saturday.

"What, Edward?"

"Doesn't Katherine have a birthday next week?"

"Yes, why?" Lillie asked.

Edward cleared his throat. "I was wondering if we could celebrate it more than we did last year."

Lillie shook her head. "I don't even know how to celebrate a birthday. We never did that when I was growin' up in Mississippi."

"It's not hard. My mom just made a pretty cake and put on a candle for each year. We got to blow out the candles. It's a special memory for me."

Lillie bit her lip. It didn't seem important to her, but if Edward wanted Katherine to have a birthday cake, she would make one. She would make sure it rivaled any cake his mother ever made.

After a special meal on Katherine's birthday, Lillie brought out the cake she had labored on all day and put it in front of Katherine. "Happy birthday, Katherine."

"Oh, Mama!" Katherine exclaimed. "It's beautiful!" She gazed at the pink roses.

Edward stuck six candles in a row in the cake and lit them. "Now, Katherine, see if you can blow all them candles out."

Katherine took a deep breath and blew her hardest. The candles flickered, then went out. She giggled. "Again, Daddy?"

Edward smoothed her hair back from her forehead. "Next year you can do it again." He pulled the candles out one by one and cut a piece of cake for each of them.

"That was marvelous," Lillie said after the children were tucked in that night. "I'm glad you insisted I try. I'll admit I felt a little unsure. But Katherine didn't care. She loved it."

Edward took her hand. "You are an amazin' woman," he said. "You're a good mama, too. I would like if we could make birthday cake a tradition for our family."

Lillie nodded in agreement. She realized again three months later when it was her birthday how much that tradition meant to him. He brought her chocolates and roses and arranged for the children to stay with his parents. "Jes' you and me," he told her. "We're gonna go out for dinner."

Edward took Lillie to a high-class black restaurant. "Order whatever you want," he said expansively.

Lillie opened the menu and stared at the unfamiliar entrees. "I have no idea. You order for both of us, Ed."

"All right," he agreed. With his experience as a porter, Ed knew what he was doing. When the waiter came, Edward ordered two specials of meatloaf and baked potato.

When their meals were placed in front of them, Lillie gazed at the tasty meat slathered in red sauce. A pool of butter nestled in the potato's crater. She savored each bite. Lillie loved the evening, but she couldn't shake her feeling of inferiority over all the ways Edward's mom excelled where she knew she herself didn't. She determined more than ever to prove to Edward she was just as capable as his mother. What if Edward tired of her homespun ways? She decided to watch for ways she could please him.

One of those ways was accompanying him on outings. One night they strolled through the park and stopped to let the children swing and slide. "Eddie?" Katherine asked. "Wanna try out this teeter-totter?"

Eddie nodded. "You get on first," he said, knowing he was heavier.

Katherine got on one end and pushed hard with both feet. Eddie caught the other end, and he climbed on. He pushed hard. "Whee!" Katherine cried when the teeter-totter bumped under her. She pushed again, and they sailed up and down, up and down.

Edward and Lillie sat close by on a park bench. "I wish this evening could go on forever," Lillie mused. "The children are havin' such fun."

After tiring of the teeter-totter, the children swooshed down the slide, sailed high on the swings, and rode the merry-go-round.

As the sun set, Edward called to them. "Come on, children, we'd better start for home."

"Already?" Katherine asked. "It seems we just started playin'." After one last trip down the slide, they skipped up to their parents, breathless and laughing. They each grabbed a hand and together they walked home.

When there wasn't machine work to do at Grapple, Lillie worked on the assembly line with the other women sorting zipper parts into boxes.

"I won't work next to that nigger," the red-headed woman called loudly one day, lifting her pug nose high in the air.

"Oh, yes, you will," Thelma, another worker, said. "We have to work together. You know what the boss said."

The red-headed woman swore. Lillie ignored her sassy comments and simply stuck to her work. As time went on, the other women soon included her, and she became one of them. At break, the women offered her cigarettes and beer. Wanting to be accepted, she took a cigarette. Soon she was not only smoking, but drinking regularly as well.

One day as Lillie worked on the assembly line, the woman standing next to her confided. "My life is so hard. I don't have a good husband. He drinks up all our money, and sometimes I don't have money for the next meal."

"I'm truly sorry," Lillie said, her fingers working metal parts as she talked. She compared her marriage with the one this woman was locked into, and her sympathy grew stronger.

The woman continued. "All my money goes for food for my children. They need clothes so badly. I wish I had money to buy some."

How can I help her? Lillie thought. *We don't have much money either, but at least we have a happy home and enough money to buy clothes for the children.*

Finishing up the set of sliders she was sorting, she went to pull a ticket from the dispenser so she could be paid according to the number of sets she had sorted. As she grabbed for a ticket, two tickets came off in her hand. She started putting the extra one back when she had a sudden thought. *This would help my dear friend.* She waited until no one was watching, then quickly put the extra ticket on her neighbor's pile. It meant the woman would get extra pay that day, and would have more money to put food on her table. *It ain't really cheatin',* Lillie reasoned. *It ain't for my benefit.*

But the next day, Lillie pulled an extra ticket on purpose. *Cheating is wrong.* Her conscience smote her. But as she did it day after day, her conscience quit speaking. Eventually she didn't think twice about her dishonesty. After all, she was helping a fellow worker in need. "Thank you, Lillie," her neighbor whispered one day. Her eyes filled with tears. "Because of you I bought winter coats for my children."

Lillie swallowed hard as her heart smote her again. She smiled bravely.

"Just tryin' to help you out," she said.

Once a month, the Grapple employees gathered for a breakfast social. Lillie took her turn hosting the event at her home. At first she felt awkward entertaining her coworkers since she was the only black person among them, but over time she earned their respect, and most of them began to accept her and treat her as an equal. The morning of the social, she set her table with the fine china Edward had recently bought her. Thelma, who had become a close friend, helped her fry the sausage and make the biscuits. "Just like Mammaw's." Lillie surveyed the pan of golden brown fluffy biscuits she had just pulled out of the oven.

Edward, always personable and courteous, made their guests feel at home. The workers lingered. "Do you think blacks will ever have any rights?" Thelma asked the group around the table.

The discussion grew animated as everyone had an opinion to share. The civil rights movement, sparked several years previously by Martin Luther King Jr.'s call to peaceful resistance of oppression, had stirred up public awareness of both systemic injustices and personal prejudices.[1]

"I can't believe how we treated you when you first came to Grapple," one woman confessed. "Now you're just one of us."

Lillie smiled. Of course, not all her coworkers treated her well—especially the red-haired woman who continually insulted her. But Lillie rejoiced to see the walls of prejudice crumble. Now that her coworkers had accepted her as a friend, perhaps they would be more supportive of blacks being integrated into society.

Sensing potential for change, Lillie began to boldly work for equality for her children. She enrolled them in white schools, and was surprised to see they were more accepted than she ever thought possible. But in spite of the progress made toward equality, painful incidents reminded the children of who they were.

One day, seven-year-old Katherine came home from school with her hair ribbons untied and her dress ripped. Her face was streaked with tears. "Katherine!" Lillie exclaimed. "What happened?"

Katherine burst into tears. "Some boys came and pulled my hair. They called me a 'no-good nigger.' I tried to run away, but one of them caught my dress and ripped it. Now I'm 'fraid it's ruined."

Lillie felt anger rise within her. She could take it if people treated her wrongly, but when someone mistreated her children, all her protective motherly instincts rose up in defensive anger. She marched Katherine to school the next day. She knocked on the teacher's door and then stepped inside, putting a protective arm around her daughter's shoulder. "Mr. Smith," she said, "I'd be mighty appreciative if you wouldn't 'llow my daughter to be harassed because she is black."

"I'm sorry." Mr. Smith's brow creased in concern. "What happened?"

Lillie told the story. "I hope you'll see that it never happens again."

"I will deal with those students today," Mr. Smith said. "She won't get treatment like that in the future."

"Thank you," Lillie said. She kissed Katherine's forehead and pushed her toward the teacher. "Go, Katherine. Try again." Lillie knew if she didn't leave quickly she might have some choice words with the students herself. But she would leave that to the teacher. *Remember what Pappaw taught you,* she reminded herself firmly. *We gotta forgive. Now I've gotta pass that lesson on to my children.*

The next day, Katherine skipped into the house. "Mama," she said, "I have a friend now. Her name is Mae. She's white."

"She is?" Lillie thought about Sue, her one white childhood friend.

"Yes, and she said she likes me better than any other girl in school. She says she likes my fuzz ball hair."

"That's nice," Lillie said.

"Mama, do you think I could invite her over for my birthday next week?"

Lillie cringed. "Oh, Katherine, it's nice to be friends with white girls, but sometimes they can't play with black girls because their parents won't let them."

"Not Mae. She would come. I'm sure she would. Please, Mama, can I invite her?"

Reluctantly Lillie gave her permission. Katherine sat down and carefully printed a pretty invitation. She drew flowers around the edge and wrote inside:

*You are invited to my eighth birthday party
at my house on Saturday.
Please come!*

The next day, Katherine burst in the door after school. "Mae thinks she can come, Mama."

"Let's wait and see before we get our hopes up." Lillie smiled down at her daughter.

Saturday came, and at 6:00, Lillie watched as Katherine gazed down the street. Her own heart tightened at the thought of her daughter's possible dashed hopes. "Here she comes! Here she comes!" Katherine jumped up and down excitedly.

Lillie opened the door to a sweet little girl. "Come in," she said kindly.

"Hi, my name is Mae," she said. She held out a prettily wrapped box. "This is for Katherine. She's my best friend."

Soon Lillie served the refreshments, and the two girls had great fun eating cake and drinking lemonade.

"Now, open your present," Mae said, clapping her hands.

Katherine carefully tore the paper off the boxed puzzle. "Oh, Mae, thank you. Shall we put it together?"

"Oh, yes," Mae said. They sat side by side finding one piece after another until they had completed the puzzle.

Lillie's heart burst with emotion as she watched her daughter playing with a little white girl. "This is what I always dreamed of," she whispered to herself as she turned to tackle the stack of dirty dishes in the kitchen.

chapter seventeen

"You're Crazy, Lillie!"

One weekend Edward took the children camping. Lillie decided to stay home this time. She lacked Edward's fondness for adventure, and she liked having time alone. She flipped on the television and found a channel where an evangelist was preaching. "God is here, God is there, God is everywhere," he declared. Lillie shifted uncomfortably. *What if God was beside me when I took those extra payroll tickets?* She banished that thought quickly.

After a moment, Lillie changed channels. She didn't feel like hearing about God. It reminded her too much of Pappaw. *I don't want to think about him,* she thought. *What would he say about my smoking and drinking? And my cheating at work?* Her cheeks burned. Pushing her shame aside, she surfed through the other stations. But when she could find nothing that interested her, she hesitantly switched back to the channel and listened to the sermon the evangelist was preaching. "You need God. I need God. We all need God. Kneel down now and accept your Savior."

Tears started running down Lillie's face. She had tried to be a good person and live with integrity, but she knew she had failed miserably. *He's right,* she thought. *I do need God.* She knelt down and prayed earnestly. "Lawd, I ain't lookin' for jes' religion, I'm lookin' for the same God my Pappaw had. If you be Him, I invite you to live in me." As she confessed her sins and poured out her heart to God, she felt a huge burden roll off her.

Her mind and heart in a jumble of tumultuous emotions, she headed absently to the kitchen. Opening the fridge out of force of habit, Lillie wanted to reach for the six-pack of beer she had bought yesterday. Her hand refused to move toward it. "No, Lillie," she heard a still, small voice. "It's not my will for you to drink."

Startled, she walked into the living room to get her cigarettes. The same presence followed her and kept her from lighting up and getting her nicotine fix. "But I need something," she cried.

"All you need is me," the voice told her.

She looked down at the immodest blouse she was wearing. "I want you to cover yourself." Again the voice was speaking. Ashamed, she hurried upstairs to change into something more decent.

"Praise de Lawd," she shouted as she walked out to sit on the front porch swing. She prayed and wept. "God, I know you're beside me."

Down the street, two black boys pushed their car. "Boys," Lillie yelled. "I'm saved, I'm saved, I'm saved. Glory hallelujah!"

The boys laughed. "If you got God like you think you do, come get this car started for us."

Lillie ran down the street and laid her hand on the car. "In the name of Jesus," she prayed, "let this car start." With the faith of her Pappaw in her heart, she had no doubt of God's power.

Skeptical, the boys cranked it again. It turned over once, then twice, then sputtered to a start.

The boys' mouths dropped open. "Don't know what you have, lady, but we'll remember you if we ever need any prayin' done again."

The sky was bluer, the clouds were whiter, and the world looked beautiful. Lillie even felt love for the white folks who had mistreated her people. "Pappaw, you would be so happy if you saw me now," she said aloud.

Soon Lillie saw Edward bringing the children home. She met them with a smile. "I'm saved, Ed! I'm saved!"

"From what?" he asked sarcastically. "From me?"

Lillie pretended not to hear him. She kissed her children. "Jesus loves you too."

They both looked bewildered. What had gotten into their mama? Was she crazy?

Lillie couldn't get done telling her family and friends about her new life. "I'm saved, I'm saved, I'm really saved!"

She witnessed on the street all the time. "Jesus died for you. Where's your joy? Just 'cept Jesus and you have joy! Praise de Lawd. Whoo!" Lillie leaped for joy.

"You're crazy, Lillie," Thelma told her. "I don't know what happened to you, but you're loony."

"I ain't loony," Lillie insisted. "Jesus fill me with such joy I can't keep my mouth shut." At night Lillie went to bed with a peace she had never had before.

One evening when Edward came home from work, Lillie could tell he was upset. "What's wrong, Ed?" she asked.

"Lillie, I've had it with your new religion." He grabbed her shoulder. "What do you think you're doin'?"

"Just witnessin'," she said. "I got such joy I want others to get the same."

Edward's grim face startled her. "I gotta go to the police station."

"Police station? Why?" Lillie asked.

"Someone reported you." His voice was accusing. "I need to go see what I can do for you. I love you, but you've been so crazy lately, I'm beginning to wonder if there is something wrong with you. I need to defend you before they throw you in jail."

Lillie's eyes got big. "I'll go along. I caused it, so I need to defend myself."

"Don't worry, children," Lillie called over her shoulder as she followed Ed out to the car. "We'll be back soon." The children sat quietly on the porch watching their strange new mama drive away.

Edward and Lillie walked into the police station together. Lillie could feel her husband's displeasure over her sudden change in behavior. How she wished he could understand! She glanced at him, standing stiffly beside her, as they waited until the detective was available. Finally the detective beckoned them to step up to his desk. He looked at the couple over his gold-rimmed glasses. "Are you Lillie Clark?"

"I am," Lillie said.

"I hear complaints about you. I have people telling me your mental state is in question, and I want to know the truth," he said.

"It's not as bad as people are saying," Edward said, trying to smooth it over. "I've been married to Lillie for twelve years, and she's never had any mental problems before."

Lillie laughed. "I am crazy 'bout Jesus. Is that what you be hearin'?"

The detective grimaced. "You are crazy. Here, have a drink." He held out a can of beer.

"I ain't crazy in the head," Lillie insisted. "And I don't drink beer no more. My God told me I ain't to take one more drink."

"Lillie," Edward pleaded. "You're not making sense! No wonder people think you're crazy."

The detective silently picked up the phone. "Hello, is this the mental health center?" he asked. Pause. "Ok, I need to make an appointment." Pause. "Lillie Clark is the name." He wrote down the date and place and handed it to Lillie. "I ask you to keep this appointment."

"I'm sorry, Ed," Lillie said on the way home. "I know you're 'shamed of me, but how can I keep quiet when my Jesus saved me?"

Ed mumbled to himself, shook his head in disgust, but didn't answer.

The next day, Ed left for work as usual. Lillie drove herself to the mental health department. As she drove, she prayed, "Lawd, you let me get into this mess. How do I get out? I'm not crazy. I'm jes' witnessin' for you."

She was shown to a little room, and waited for the doctor, hands folded on her purse. The doctor soon came in. "What's going on in your life?"

Lillie witnessed to the woman. "I'm not crazy. I jes' got the joy of Jesus. And I guess it makes others uncomfortable." Lillie went on to tell her whole story, becoming more animated as she went. She suddenly realized her hands were waving in the air. With a quick glance at the doctor, she folded them back on top of her purse and waited.

The doctor jotted down some notes. She sat looking at Lillie for a long time. "Lillie," she said. "I don't think you are a mental case. I suggest you get your life balanced out and then come back. Then I can make some recommendations."

So Lillie went home and told Ed what the doctor had said. "I ain't plannin' to go back neither."

Ed thought a long time, smoking. Finally he crushed out his cigarette. "I think we just need to give this some time. I think the doctor is right. You will balance out soon."

Lillie didn't want her marriage to fall apart. Not after all the good years they'd had together. But she also had to be obedient to the Holy Spirit. When Jesus told her something, she had to listen. But as much as she could honor her husband, she did.

One day Edward wanted to take the children fishing. Now eight and ten, they were both old enough to enjoy it. "Mama, come with us," they begged. "You never come with us anymore."

Lillie shook her head. "I'm staying home. I want some uninterrupted time to read my Bible. I promise I will go with you next time."

Edward studied her with narrowed eyes. He shook his head briefly. "I don't understand you, Lillie. Before you got this Jesus business, you always did things with us, but now you just want to stay at home."

Lillie's heart ached for Edward. He couldn't understand her desire for time alone with God, but she didn't let that discourage her. She packed up her husband and children and sent them out the door with sleeping bags and fishing poles. "Bye, Mama," they shouted. "We're gonna have us a good time."

"Bye." Lillie waved as they left with Edward. She felt a twinge of guilt for staying home, but she felt her need of time alone with God. She sat on the front porch with her Bible. "Lawd, I want to know more about you. Please show me."

Looking up, Lillie saw an old black woman coming up her walk. "Are you Lillie Clark?" she asked.

"Yes," Lillie said, surprised this woman knew her name.

"My name is Sister Jenkins. God told me today to come visit you."

"He did? Well, praise de Lawd. I need some encouragin' 'bout now."

"Yes, I would like to take you to church with me. You need instruction in God's way and baptism into a church."

"I do?" Lillie was startled.

"Yes, it's all in the Bible. Do you read it?"

"I do," Lillie said fervently. She lifted her Bible from her lap to show the lady.

"Let me read you a story," Sister Jenkins said. She sat down on the swing next to Lillie. Taking Lillie's Bible and turning to Acts 16, she read how Paul and Silas sat in prison. Then she explained, "And at midnight, their stocks fell off and an angel led them out of prison. The jailor wanted to kill himself, but the prisoners led him to the Lawd. He was baptized with all those of his house."

Lillie's heart ached. "I wish my family would be doin' this with me, but I was jes' askin' God to show me what the next step is. I think God wants me to come to your church."

"You would be welcome," Sister Jenkins said. "We try to live according to God's Word. We be Apostolics."

"My Pappaw and Mammaw always attended a Methodist church, but I don't s'pose God cares which church I go to."

Sister Jenkins smiled and nodded. "Our God is bigger than any denomination."

The next day, Edward brought the children home. "Mama," Eddie cried, running in the door. "You missed out on so much fun!"

Lillie hugged them all and helped them take care of their smoky, wet camping gear. "Ed," she said, as she worked. "I was wonderin' if you would attend church with me on Sunday."

Ed's face turned hard. "Don't push your Jesus on me."

"I'm not. I'm only askin'."

Sunday, Lillie got up early and quietly got ready to go to church. Ed and the children were still sleeping when she left the house. Sister Jenkins stopped to pick her up in her car. "Your family is welcome to come too," she said.

"I wish I could get them to come with me." Lillie sounded discouraged. "But my husband doesn't love my Jesus."

"That's too bad," Sister Jenkins said. "You must be careful to win him by your 'chaste conversation,' like the Scripture says."[1]

What does she mean by that? Lillie asked herself. She determined to look in the Bible for answers.

When they walked into the vestibule, a canvas on the wall drew Lillie's attention. An artist had illustrated two roads—a wide luxurious road and a narrow winding path. Lillie looked at the wide road. Sunshine, crowds of people, pleasure, money, and so many tempting things adorned the way. At the end of this path was a huge gaping hole with people falling into it. Then she noticed the other path. Lightning, few people, thorns, and suffering. Nothing on that path looked inviting. But at the end of this path, golden light encircled a gate to happiness. Lillie stood there entranced. "Lawd, show me more," she prayed.

"Come, Lillie," Sister Jenkins called. "It's time for the service to start."

Lillie followed her new friend and sat down beside her. People crowded into the small sanctuary. Lillie noticed families sitting together. The women's sleeves covered their elbows. Their dresses swept low to the floor. Lillie remembered how immodest she felt the day she gave her heart to the Lord.

"God wants us to live holy and righteous," the pastor taught from the pulpit. "Husbands, love your wives. Wives, honor your husbands. Forsake your sins, dress modestly, and put away your cigarettes."

Lillie soaked up the teaching she was hearing for the first time. Now some of the convictions God had laid on her heart made more sense. As she learned to know God, she felt her love for Ed grow stronger. She wanted to honor him in every way she could, even though he didn't love God like she did. Perhaps she could make up for the rift that seemed to be growing between them.

After the service, Lillie met the pastor. "Thank you, Pastor, for your words today. I will be back next Sunday."

"God bless you, Sister. You will be blessed by your hunger to hear God's Word."

chapter eighteen

Baptism and a Trip South

"An' all his household believed and was baptized!"[1] The pastor's voice rose emphatically. Lillie stirred in her seat on the pew. The pastor was talking about the household of Cornelius. How Lillie wished her husband would believe! Even though Edward tried to do right, she knew he hadn't experienced salvation.

The next morning, Lillie pondered the account of Cornelius. Once again the phrase jumped out at her: "And was baptized." Suddenly, she knew she must take that step of faith.

Lillie approached the pastor the following Sunday. "Pastor," she said. "I understood from your message from God last Sunday that I, like Cornelius, need to be baptized. How do I go 'bout it?"

The pastor led her through a few sessions of instruction, then announced to the church that Lillie would be baptized the next Sunday. If anyone had any counsel to give, they were asked to speak to the pastor soon.

Lillie prayed about how she would ask Edward about coming to her baptism. "Ed," she said after the children went to bed Saturday night, "tomorrow is a very special day for me. Would you consider bringin' the children to church tomorrow morning? I'm gonna be baptized as a believer, and I'd jes' love to share this day with my family."

To Lillie's amazement, Edward agreed. "But don't think we're gonna come every time."

Lillie's heart felt full as she walked into church with her family. They sat on the front bench with Lillie. She had a hard time containing her joy. Her children glanced at her occasionally as she wriggled in her seat.

The pastor got up. "We have assembled today to celebrate the new life in Sister Lillie Clark's life. She has asked to be baptized, and we have not received any negative counsel or reasons not to go through with this." He motioned to Lillie. "You can follow me into the water."

Robed in white, Lillie rose and walked into the baptistery filled with warm water. The pastor eased her backward into the water until her head was submerged. The water washed over her, and then she heard the sound of the pastor's voice as her head came back out of the water. "In Jesus' name I baptize you," his rich, deep voice rang out as he helped her stand again. "God bless you, Sister Lillie. Now you will walk in newness of life." He led her out of the pool and handed her a towel.

Lillie dried herself as best as she could, then walked into the arms of Sister Jenkins.

Edward had sat there uncomfortably watching this strange and unfamiliar spiritual ritual. He awkwardly walked up to Lillie and put his arm around her shoulder.

The children followed. Lillie grabbed them both in her arms and hugged them. "You're wet," Eddie said, wiping at his shirt. "Now I'm all drippin'."

Lillie laughed. She felt so lighthearted she thought her feet might lift off the floor. She seemed to float home with her husband and children. The children ate quietly, then curled up in chairs to read. How she wished her Pappaw could see her now! He would be so happy with her new life.

Maybe I should go visit my grandparents, she thought.

"Ed," she asked, "I have one more request. I would like to go tell Pappaw and Mammaw about my new life. I know you've never met 'em, but I really feel a need to see 'em b'fore they die."

Ed consented, and the following week, he took them to the station and bought the tickets for Lillie, Katherine, and Eddie. As the train steamed in, he kissed them goodbye. "What am I gonna do without my family?" He hugged them all. Then taking Lillie by the hand, he walked with them to the closest coach. "Hey, Tom," he said to the porter. "Don't tell me they haven't promoted you yet."

"Hey, Edward, haven't seen you on this train in a long time." Tom put a stool on the platform and turned to help Lillie into the train.

"Yeah, they put me on a different line. Wouldn't mind if they let me come back to this one."

Tom laughed. "Sure do miss you, Ed."

"My family is going to Mississippi. I'm puttin' them in your good care, Tom."

"I'll watch over them, Ed, I will."

Lillie climbed onto the train, then waved a kiss toward Edward standing by the station. He waved back.

"Mama?" Katherine asked. "Where do we sit?"

Lillie helped them find their seats. The children plastered their faces against the window. "Daddy Ed, Daddy Ed," they called, waving. "We are gonna have fun. Our first train ride."

Eddie and Katherine couldn't sit still. "Mama, can we walk around a little?" Eddie asked.

"I guess," Lillie said. "Just don't go too far away." Another little girl came to her mind—a girl who had traveled many years ago from the very place they were returning to. She remembered the thrill of riding the train cars for the first time. She leaned back against the seat and sighed. She had exhausted herself getting everything ready for this trip.

Soon the children were back. They sat with their noses pressed to the window watching the landscape streak past. Finally, the sun slipped behind the hills, and darkness fell. "When will we be there, Mama?" Katherine asked sleepily.

"We'll get there tomorrow mornin'. It's time for both of you to try to sleep." She reclined their seats and covered them each with a blanket from their luggage. They soon drifted off to sleep.

Next thing they knew, Lillie woke them up. "We'll soon be seein' Canton," she said as she shook them.

They sat up, yawned, and rubbed the sleep out of their eyes. As the train rumbled into the Canton station, memories flooded Lillie's mind. The town had changed. Cars drove on the roads instead of wagons. All the buildings on Main Street had been painted.

They disembarked and Lillie led the children down the street through town. "Mama," Katherine said. "It's busy here like Clearmill."

Lillie hadn't made any plans on how to get out to the old plantation, but she hoped she might find someone in town who would take her. She headed to the mercantile where Pappaw had kept an account long ago. Just as she lifted the latch to open the door, she heard someone.

"Can it be Lillie?" a voice called.

Lillie turned to see who it was. "Sutter," Lillie cried, running to her old-time school friend. "God knew I needed to see someone familiar in this town. I thought the town had forgotten all about me."

The years melted away as Sutter loaded Lillie and her children into her car and headed into the country. They had only a few minutes to catch up on each other's lives. "Are you married and happy in Clearmill?" Sutter asked.

"Yes, Edward provides for us so well. What about you, Sutter?"

"I married a doctor. Life is still hard, but he provides well for me."

"I'm so happy for you." Lillie turned her attention to the familiar yet foreign landscape that sped by her window. It had been so long.

Soon they reached the old plantation. As Sutter stopped in front of a shack, Lillie could only stare. "Is this it?" Weeds grew close to the cabin where the fields hadn't been tilled or farmed. The shack looked more dilapidated than she remembered.

"Yes, it's the same place," Sutter said. "Your grandparents aren't as young as they used to be. It's a lot for them to keep up with."

Disappointed, Lillie nodded. She sat a moment longer. *It's the people who matter*, she reminded herself, *not places*. Then she jumped out of the car, flew up onto the porch, and burst in the door. "Pappaw! Mammaw!" she cried. "I'm here."

Two old people raised their heads from the table where they had been reading their Bibles. "Lillie?" Pappaw wavered.

"Lillie?" Mammaw chorused. "Is it really Lillie?"

"Yes, Pappaw. Yes, Mammaw. It's Lillie." She ran to them and hugged them. They had more wrinkles than she remembered, but otherwise they still looked the same.

Lillie turned and motioned to her children. She led them forward and put an arm around each of them. "This is Edward Jr. and Katherine," she said.

"Well, I'll be. They're the prettiest things I saw since you were little," Pappaw said.

Lillie laughed. "I've told 'em so much about Pappaw and Mammaw, and I wanted 'em to meet you."

"Can you stay for a while?" Pappaw asked eagerly.

"Of course," Lillie said. "We didn't come all this way jes' to turn around and leave again."

Pappaw's wrinkled face broke into a big smile. He got up and limped out the door. He grabbed the bags out of the car and carried them back into the house.

"Thank you for bringin' us, Sutter," Lillie said. "Why don't you come in and visit with us awhile?"

Sutter shook her head. "You need time with your grandparents. I'll catch up with you later. I need to get home to my family anyway. If you let me know, I'll gladly taxi you back to Canton."

"I'll get word to you." Lillie waved as Sutter's car drove away.

"Now, Mammaw," Lillie scolded as Mammaw shuffled to the kitchen. "You let me make the biscuits and brew the tea. You sit down and talk to me."

"But, Lillie," Mammaw sputtered.

"I insist," Lillie said, putting Mammaw's apron around her own waist.

"Oh, all right," Mammaw conceded with a chuckle. She slowly sat down at the table. "I just tire out easy these days."

Lillie soon had tea ready. "Come, children. Sit and eat biscuits at the table where your mama ate many a breakfast."

Eddie and Katherine shyly sat down. Quietly, they drank their tea and ate a biscuit. "Can we go outside and play?" Eddie asked Pappaw.

"O' course," he said. "Later, I'll show you everythin'. We'll get to know each other."

The children scampered away to explore.

"Pappaw," Lillie said. "I wanted to come tell you myself what has happened in my life. Your prayers followed me. I've been saved! Praise de Lawd! But now people think I'm a crazy woman. And I think my husband even wonders."

Pappaw chuckled. "Praise de Lawd! I've been prayin' for years, not knowin' what God's a-doin' up there in Pennsylvania. Don't give that devil no reason to be laughin' at you. You be strong and lovin' the Lawd. You hear me now?"

Lillie felt comforted by Pappaw's words. She remembered him telling her he was misunderstood many times in his Christian life. "God will be with ya," he said.

A week flew past, then two. Lillie knew she needed to return to Clearmill and Edward. But her soul was being fed, and her children spent the days exploring the whole plantation with Pappaw.

Finally, after three weeks, she packed their bags to leave. "Mama Lillie?" Katherine asked wistfully. "Do we have to leave? I like it here with Pappaw and Mammaw."

Lillie sighed. "I know. I do too. But your daddy is missin' you, I know. We need to get home to him."

"I suppose so," Katherine said. "Maybe he could just come down here."

Lillie laughed. "Your daddy wouldn't like Mississippi very much. His home is in Clearmill, and we need to go back to him."

She carried her bags out of the house and set them on the front porch. "Pappaw, Mammaw, I wish you would come with us to Pennsylvania."

"No, chile, we love our Mississippi. This is our country," Pappaw said. "We wanna die here. But it gave our weary bones a lotta joy to see you again. We send our love to Edward."

Lillie kissed them both, and her children hugged them. Sutter waited in the car. "Goodbye," they called as they drove away. Lillie turned to see her grandparents waving on their front porch. Would this be the last time she would see them alive?

chapter nineteen

The Cost of Obedience

When Lillie stepped down from the train, she knew she had truly come home. Edward tenderly kissed her when he met her. "How I missed you!" he said. "My whole life was gone. I walked around here like a homeless kitten."

Katherine laughed. "You shoulda come with us, Daddy. You woulda liked Pappaw and Mammaw. And besides, we saw where Mama lived when she was a little girl."

Edward put an arm around Katherine's shoulder. "So you didn't want to come back?"

"Not at first," Katherine admitted, hanging her head. "I thought maybe I wanted to stay there, but now I'm glad I came back."

"Pappaw showed us all over the big plantation," Eddie added. "Lots of places to explore there."

Edward chuckled as he slapped his son on the back. "Good thing you came back. I woulda missed you if you'd have stayed there."

Eddie grinned. "Mama Lillie said we had to come back 'cuz you would be missing us."

Edward smiled at Lillie. "I'm glad you took that trip with the children. Showin' 'em their roots will be the best thing you ever did for them, don't you think?"

Lillie shook her head. "Roots are important. But the best thing I could do is teach them to love the same Lawd I do."

"Oh," Edward said slowly, his grin fading. "I was hopin' some time away would help you forget."

A deep sadness crept into Lillie's heart. How she wished her husband would understand, and how she wished they could live this life together for the Lord!

The next morning, Lillie clocked in on time for her shift at Grapple. Mr. Hanstine, the boss, pulled her aside. "Good to have you back, Lillie."

"Good to be home. Thanks for givin' me some time off," Lillie said.

"You deserved it," Mr. Hanstine said. "But one thing has been bothering me. I thought I would face it head on when you got back. You can't be witnessing all over this plant. It makes people uncomfortable."

"I only have the joy of Jesus," Lillie said. "And I jes' want to share my joy."

"You can do it in private," Mr. Hanstine said, "but not in public."

"All right." But she just couldn't help herself. She quit witnessing in public as her boss had told her to, but she still put Bibles in the employee bathrooms, in the big shots' offices, and in all their conference rooms. She even left tracts in her fellow employees' lockers.

One day she got caught. She was busily putting tracts into lockers and didn't hear footsteps behind her. "So it's you spreading falsehoods around here?" Schwinn, a new employee, called.

"Jesus is the way, the truth, and the life," Lillie replied. She put her tracts back into her locker and turned to leave.

"So you really believe in J.C.?" he asked.

"Jesus Christ is Lawd," Lillie said firmly. She waved her hand. "See ya tomorrow."

The next morning, Schwinn met her with a sneer. "How's J.C. doing today?"

"My Jesus Christ lives in my heart," Lillie told him. "You can't never insult me with your words."

She walked with him to the machines where they would be working that day. "If your J.C. is as powerful as you think He is, pray over this machine. It refuses to work." Schwinn pointed to the silent silver monster.

Lillie calmly laid her hand on the machine. "In the name of Jesus, I command you to run."

Schwinn laughed. "You really expect J.C. will make it run?" He reached over and pushed the start button. The machine roared to life. "U-h-h!" Schwinn stuttered.

"Thank you, Jesus, for hearin' my prayer." Lillie knew Pappaw's prayers followed her. How she longed to be near her Pappaw's strong faith again. She had found an inner strength while spending time with him those three short weeks.

One day, the red-haired woman was beside Lillie on the assembly line. "Do you know how much I detest that flowered dress?" She followed her insult with a cuss.

Lillie started at the sharp words. "N–no," she stammered. "It's my only dress fit to wear."

"I don't care." The woman's eyes sparked. "If you wear it again, I'm gonna rip it off you."

Lillie looked down at her dress. She walked slowly home thinking about what that woman had said. She washed the dress carefully as she did each night and hung it up to dry. "I ain't got nothing else to wear," Lillie lamented to her husband that night.

"She surely can't be serious," Edward said.

"I dunno," Lillie said. "She looked pretty serious to me."

"Well, we'll buy you another one," Edward said, laughing.

The next day, Lillie wore her flowered dress as she always did. She tried to enter quietly but was spotted immediately by the woman. Hands on hips, the redhead stood blocking the entrance. Taking a handful of Lillie's dress in her fist, the woman pulled. "I told you not to wear this ugly thing anymore," the woman said. The dress tore as she jerked the front open. Buttons popped off.

"Praise de Lawd anyway," Lillie cried, groping to close the torn dress.

Lillie's friend Thelma saw it happen and marched over to them. She positioned herself between the two ladies. "You might be praising the Lord, but I'm going to beat her up!"

"It's just a dress. I can get another one," Lillie said. She hurried to gather up the buttons so she could sew them back on.

Thelma turned to the redhead. "You should be ashamed of yourself."

"It's all right," Lillie said. "You need to love her anyway." She steadfastly repeated the theme that governed her life, "We gotta love folks even when they wrong us."

Thelma turned away without saying more, but Lillie knew she was furious. Lillie found some pins and closed up the gaps where the buttons had been.

At home that evening, Lillie told Edward what had happened. He shook his head. "I didn't think she was serious. Shall I wring her neck for you?"

Lillie laughed. "No, it was just a dress."

"Come, we are going to buy you another one."

Later that evening, Edward and Lillie drove to town. He picked out three new dresses for her that were simple but also pretty and modest. Lillie smiled as she hung the dresses on hangers and placed them in her closet.

The next day, Lillie wore one of her new dresses. The redhead met her at the door with a dozen roses. "I'm sorry, Lillie, it was mean of me to do what I did yesterday," she said. "I really do like you. I don't know what made me do that."

Beaming, Lillie hugged her. "It's no matter. I needed to get me a different dress, and I guess now I did. You got the joy of the Lawd in your heart?"

The redhead shook her head. "I don't know what you have, but it sure makes a difference in your life."

For the rest of her shift, Lillie couldn't get those words out of her head. *It makes a difference in your life.* She knew she had cheated the company for a long while. But she had reasoned she wasn't cheating if she was helping someone else. Even so, she still knew Jesus wanted her to tell her boss now. With heart pounding and feet dragging, she headed toward her boss's office after she clocked out.

"Mr. Hanstine?" She timidly opened his office door.

"What is it, Lillie?" he asked. "Come inside."

She quietly closed the door behind her. Leaning her back against it, she said, "I got somethin' I need to tell you."

Mr. Hanstine rolled his eyes. "I hope it isn't more of this J.C. stuff."

Lillie wrung her hands. "My Jesus would have every right to be 'shamed of me right now. But I wasn't saved durin' all my workin' days here. But now I know what I did was wrong."

Mr. Hanstine put his elbows on his desk. "What was that?"

Lillie told him everything—how she felt sorry for the poor worker and slipped her extra tickets when no one was looking. "I know I cheated the company, and I'm sorry."

Mr. Hanstine stroked his chin. "That's stealing, Lillie. I could throw you out for it."

"I know, Mr. Hanstine. Is that what you're gonna do?"

Mr. Hanstine pursed his lips and sat silently for a long time. He sighed. "You have always been a good worker, Lillie. And I know you didn't mean to steal. But I can't keep you. It would be bad for my company and my reputation to allow a thief to continue working."

Lillie nodded. "I understand."

"I wish I didn't have to let you go, Lillie," Mr. Hanstine said. "After everyone forgets about it, you can come back and see if there would be a job for you."

Lillie shook her head. "I need a job now. I doubt I will be back. Thank you, Mr. Hanstine, for giving me a chance. You have made me feel like a regular American citizen and not a black woman who has been discriminated against."

Mr. Hanstine shook her hand. "And I've never been sorry I hired you. We are losing a valuable employee today."

"Thank you, Mr. Hanstine," Lillie said quietly.

She walked back through the building she had worked in for ten years. She looked at each machine she had conquered and thought about the good times she'd had while she worked there. "I'm gonna miss you," she said softly. Fortunately the Grapple employees had all gone home. She didn't want to face them today. As she left the building, the door slammed behind her for the last time.

She took her time walking home. She had some talking to do with her Jesus before she met Edward. He would not understand what she had done today.

That night at supper, Lillie joked nervously, "Well, my dress is ripped off me one day, and the next I come home with no job."

Edward looked at her with questions in his eyes. Lillie explained her dishonesty and how Mr. Hanstine had to let her go. "He had no choice," Lillie defended him.

"But you weren't stealin' for yourself," Edward said. "Why did you have to tell him?"

"My Jesus asks me to be honest. I couldn't get 'round it. I had to confess."

Edward stared at his wife. "Will I ever understand you?" he asked.

"Not until you find Jesus. Don't worry, I'll find other work," she promised.

chapter twenty

Goodbyes

"Katherine," Lillie said one Saturday morning. "How would you like to help me make biscuits?"

Katherine grinned. "Yes, Mama, let's! Just like the ones you made at Mammaw's house."

Standing side by side at the kitchen table, they measured flour, baking powder, lard, salt, and buttermilk into a bowl. "Now let's knead it with our hands," Lillie said. Flour and bits of sticky dough soon covered their fingers.

Together, they rolled out little circles and placed them in rows on the pan to put in the oven. "I like baking with you, Mama," Katherine said. "You haven't spent much time with us since we got back from Mississippi."

Lillie's heart squeezed with hurt. *I should be spending more time with my children,* she thought. In the midst of the busyness, Lillie tried hard to be a good Christian wife and mother. She enrolled Katherine and Eddie in every program available—music, swimming, wrestling, and anything else they wanted to try. She had determined to give them the childhood she never had.

She also knew she needed to spend time with her parents. Too much time had passed since she had seen them.

A few days later, she walked across town and knocked on her parents' door. "Mama Belle? Daddy James? Is anyone home?" She pushed open the door.

"Lillie!" Mama Belle exclaimed, turning from the kitchen sink. "What brings you here?"

"I came here to bring you love from Pappaw and Mammaw," Lillie said, her voice cracking.

"Pappaw and Mammaw? How so?"

"I took Eddie and Katherine to see them. I spent three weeks there. I was so encouraged in the Lawd by Pappaw's life," Lillie said glowing.

"So you got the same religion as Pappaw, huh?" Mama Belle stared at her.

"Yes, Mama Belle. Do you?"

"I can't say I do, really. Pappaw's faith was a bit radical for me. I got religion, oh, yes, I do, but not the same kind as Pappaw."

Lillie turned her face away. She didn't want Mama Belle to see her pain. "I guess I'm a radical Christian like Pappaw. He told me no one understood him, and I don't think many understand me either."

"Bring Eddie and Katherine to see us," Mama Belle pleaded, changing the subject.

"I will," Lillie promised.

Eddie would turn twelve in just a few days. Remembering how Edward valued birthday celebrations, Lillie prepared to make a cake. "What shall we get him for a gift?" she asked Edward.

"Why don't we get him one of those Parker Brothers Monopoly games? All the boys have them," Edward said.

"Won't that be expensive?" Lillie asked, worried about the cost.

Edward's eyes twinkled. "I remember how much I wanted one when they first came out. I was Eddie's age. Now I have an excuse to get one."

"Oh, you! Still a child at heart, aren't you?" Lillie's eyes twinkled.

Lillie invited her parents over for the party. "Edward likes my children to have a cake with a candle for each year," she explained.

"That's a good tradition," Mama Belle said. "We never had any money or time to really do any celebratin' when you was a girl."

After Eddie blew out his candles and the family members each enjoyed a piece of cake to celebrate, Edward invited them all into the living room so Eddie could open his gift. "Do you know what it is?" Edward asked his son.

Eddie shook his head. He ripped the pretty paper off as soon as Edward handed it to him. Eddie was overjoyed with his game. His daddy and his grandpa sat down that evening and divided out the money and started playing with Eddie. "I'll buy Park Place," Eddie told his dad.

"That's a good move, son." Edward cuffed him on the shoulder. "I hope you make those kinds of money decisions in real life."

Lillie watched from where she sat with her Mama Belle. Edward was such a good team builder. But life was more than Monopoly and Park Place. How she wished her husband would join her in the spiritual things that really mattered in this life.

Night after night, Edward and his son played Monopoly. Katherine would join them sometimes, and Lillie even tried her hand at it. "I'm no good at makin' money," she said after she went bankrupt. "I think I'll leave this here game to you."

"Mama," Katherine said thoughtfully one day after school, "sometimes I get scared that a bomb will drop on us."

"What makes you think about such things?" Lillie asked, astonished.

"I know why," said Eddie. "Today we had an atomic bomb drill at school. When the buzzer rang, we all had to run for the basement."

"I see," Lillie said. "I understand why you might be afraid of bombs. War is a scary thing, and our country is still living in fear because of the recent war. But, you know children, my faith is in Jesus as my Savior. He can take away any fear of wars, bombs, or the future."

"But Daddy says all that Jesus stuff is jes' a fairy tale." Katherine's face was full of questions.

Lillie sighed. "Your daddy has never shared my faith in Jesus. I pray often he would. But you both can, even if Daddy never does."

"We can?" Eddie asked. "But we don' like what Jesus makes you do."

Lillie smiled. "A little radical? I know I have been, but the peace Jesus brings to my heart makes me shout and witness. I don't want you to accept Jesus until He puts it in your heart, children. But I do want you to know I will pray every day that God will find you."

"But what if I'm still scared of bombs?" Katherine asked.

"I will pray God takes those fears away," Lillie said.

"All right, Mama Lillie," Katherine said. Then she leaned close and whispered in Lillie's ear. "I don't want Eddie to know, but I know God answers your prayers."

Lillie hugged her daughter tightly. "I'm glad you think so, Katherine."

One morning in November 1960, Ed read the newspaper at breakfast as usual. "Mercy," he muttered. "When will we ever be accepted as the black people we are?"

"Why do you say that?" Lillie asked.

"I just read this article about a little girl named Ruby Bridges down in

New Orleans." Ed pointed to the story. "Have you heard about it?"

"No." Lillie paused in clearing away the dishes to listen intently as he summarized what he had read.

"Ruby Bridges lived only five blocks away from an all-white elementary school, but she was forced to travel several miles every day to attend an all-black kindergarten. The state of Louisiana has been taking steps to integrate their schools, but lawmakers stalled the process by demanding that black students pass a proficiency test before being accepted at a white school. Ruby passed the test. But federal marshals had to escort her and her mother to school every day because people were so upset. She is the first black child to attend an all-white elementary school in the South. People have insulted her and threated to poison her, but her mother reminds her to be strong and pray each day as she enters school."[1]

"Go, Ruby!" Lillie cheered. "That gives me hope for Eddie and Katherine. Their lives will be better than ours. Prejudice will be overcome." Lillie's face glowed.

Edward leaned back in his chair. "Perhaps. You remember back in February I told you about the sit-in at Woolworth's restaurant?"[2]

Lillie nodded. She recalled how four African-Americans had entered a whites-only restaurant and sat down at the counter. They were refused service and asked to leave, but didn't budge even when police came and tried to force them to go.

"Some black folks don't 'cept their place in society," Edward mused. "But sometimes I wonder if more of us should be workin' to change the system."

"Mama?" Katherine's forehead furrowed in puzzlement. "Why can't we just be 'ccepted like white people are?"

"I don't know the answer," Lillie said, thinking of another girl years ago, asking the same question. "But times are changin'. I remember askin' a white boy for a drink of water, and he gave me dirty water that he had washed his hair in. Your classmates at school ain't as rude as that. Think of it—your great-grandparents were slaves, your grandparents were share-croppers, and now your parents hold decent jobs alongside white people. That should show you this nation has made progress."

"I don't know." Ed shook his head slowly as he folded the newspaper. "I jes' don't know."

Lillie applied for a job as a cook at a college in Clearmill. She felt she needed something to fill her time since her job at Grapple had been terminated. Though she realized that when she and Edward both had jobs, it put the squeeze on family time, they felt like they needed both incomes.

To her surprise, she was hired on the spot. "Can you come in at three o'clock tomorrow morning?" the supervisor asked.

"Yes, I can," Lillie answered.

While it was still dark the next morning, Lillie joined the kitchen staff at the college. She buttered dozens of loaves of bread and put them on trays for the noon meal. "Think it'll be enough?" she asked another cook.

"Mercy, yes," she said. "We ain't cookin' for the five thousand!"

But some days, Lillie felt they were.

At twelve o'clock sharp, the double doors swung open as students lunged to be first in line at the cafeteria. They grabbed a tray and helped themselves to the meat, potatoes, vegetable, and bread. Lillie replaced the trays as they emptied. She could hear snatches of conversation.

"I'm gonna grow my hair long," one young man said.

"Why'd you do that?" asked a black boy.

"Cuz my parents wouldn't like it," the first boy snickered.

Lillie could see a segment of the student body rebelling. She prayed. "Lawd, reach down and touch these young people's hearts. If you don't, somethin's gonna snap, and loud too."

When she left work in the afternoon, students stood by the sidewalk picketing against war. "Peace, not war," shouted one banner. "No more war," screamed another.

One boy stopped her. "You believe in war?" he asked.

Lillie shook her head. "No one likes war."

"Would you sign this protest against the Vietnam War, ma'am?" he asked.

Lillie raised her hand. "Whoa, I'm not a protestor. I don't believe this will get you anywhere. Get back into school, son, and learn something to really help your country."

This counterculture continued to grow. Students dropped out of school and rejected "the establishment" as they called it. They opposed middleclass values, maintained disdain for all their parents had done for them, rejected nuclear weapons, and embraced Eastern philosophy to find meaning in life. Men grew their hair long, and women used almost no makeup. "Peace, love, and personal freedom," was what they promoted. They set up a commune on the college grounds. They sang, danced, and smoked marijuana.

One evening, Lillie decided to meet these hippies head on. She walked through the campus filled with Volkswagen vans painted with colorful peace symbols. "Praise de Lawd," she shouted. "He's my Savior; He can be yours too."

She stopped in front of one van and asked, "So if it feels good, do it, right?"

The barefoot woman gave her a thumbs-up. "Sure thing, nigger."

Lillie walked on. She noticed one man dressed in ragged pants, tie-dyed shirt, and beads dangling from his wrists. She moved close. "You know Jesus?" she asked, getting in his face.

"Huh?" The man's glazed eyes didn't seem to register.

Lillie jerked up a bandana tied around the man's head. "So you do your own thing, wherever and whenever you want. Do you really think droppin' out of society is the way to happiness?"

"Yeah, sure, why not?" he said, laughing as he yanked his bandana back down over his long hair.

Lillie smelled marijuana as she approached the next huddle. "And you blow the mind of every straight person you can reach, don't you?" she asked.

The group laughed a wobbly laugh. "We feel so good!" one man shouted.

In a big grassy area, music was playing loudly. Couples danced together. Lillie shouted, "If it's not drugs, then it's romance and fun. How long does that thrill last? Tell me now!"

Not one dancer turned toward her, but a man came up behind her and caught her arm. "Whatcha think you're doing, nigger? We only want love, peace, and harmony. Please leave."

Lillie shrugged him off. "I will leave, but I want you to answer one question first. Do you love Jesus?"

"We love everyone," the man said. "If he's a person, we love him too." He led her away from the throng of hippies. "You'd better not be seen around here again. The next one might not treat you so nicely."

Lillie returned to the college kitchen with a heavy heart. She had wanted to share Jesus, but once again, people had rejected His precious name.

As time passed, Lillie watched her parents' declining health. Their hard life in the fields in the South had taken a toll on their bodies. One day when they were together, Lillie sat down and looked right into Daddy James's eyes. "You ain't feelin' so well, are you?"

Daddy James didn't say anything.

"Daddy James?" Lillie tried again.

A tear trickled down her old Daddy James's face. "I don't feel well," he admitted. "Your Mama Belle doesn't even know, but I'm getting some tests done at the doctor."

"Oh, Daddy James," Lillie said, leaning her face close to his.

Daddy James swallowed hard. "Don't tell your Mama Belle, but I wouldn't be surprised if it was some terminal illness."

"No, Daddy James," Lillie cried.

The rest of the day a cloud hovered over her. She felt sad as she left to go home. The most important thing she could do was pray while she waited for her Daddy James to get results back.

A few days later Mama Belle made plans to attend her cousin's wedding in Ohio. She caught a ride with Aunt Florence to the wedding. "Behave, Mrs. Johnson," Lillie teased her lovingly.

The next afternoon, Lillie's phone rang. "Hello, praise de Lawd!" she answered in her accustomed manner. Almost immediately, she knew something was wrong. "Lillie," her uncle's voice quavered on the other end. "Your Mama Belle isn't with us anymore."

"Not with us?" Lillie asked, bewildered.

"No, she's gone. Dead."

"Dead?" Lillie exclaimed. "How?"

"She keeled over with a heart attack at the wedding. We tried to revive her, but we couldn't. I'm ever so sorry to bring you this shockin' news."

"Oh, Mama Belle," Lillie mourned, "how can we live without you?" She called her dad to break the news as gently as she could.

Daddy James remained strong for the children. They all gathered at his house to plan the funeral. "Mama Belle would want us to be happy," Daddy James said. "She would want us to remember the good times." Lillie knew that was true, but it didn't take away the pain of parting.

Now that Mama Belle was gone, Lillie turned her whole attention to Daddy James. His test results came back, but it wasn't the news she was hoping for. Her Daddy James had cancer. His strong body wasted away quickly because of the disease, and within a year he also was gone. Even though her siblings were still alive, Lillie felt terribly alone after her parents' deaths.

chapter twenty-one

The Nest Empties

Now that her parents were both gone, Lillie put even more energy into her children's education. Edward Jr. was graduating in the spring from the Clearmill High School, where he was the only black student. Edward in his suit and tie and Lillie in her best dress arrived at the gymnasium for the ceremony. "We are proud to announce that today, for the first time, we have a black student as valedictorian of the class. Edward Clark, the floor is yours."

Lillie's eyes swam with tears as she watched her son stand up and walk across the stage to the podium. He laid his paper on the lectern and raised his eyes to the audience. Lillie smiled as he looked her way. Then he spoke:

"So here we are, class, leaving Clearmill High School. I'm a different person now than I was when I started school twelve years ago. I hope I'm a better one. I've learned so much about myself.

"Where to from here? The answer to that question is as varied as the students who make up this year's graduating class. Many of us know the next step to take, whether college or taking some job here in Clearmill.

"The biggest thing I learned is that knowledge is learned by the student who applies himself.

"To everyone who touched our lives, we say thank you. To parents who stood by us no matter what. To teachers who tried to instill in us a passion for learning. To friends who were there for parties, study sessions, and everything in between. And to all those others we depend on. Without you, there would be no purpose to being here.

"And so, Clearmill High School Class of 1966, we did it! It's a huge milestone. I'm sure we will remember this day for the rest of our lives."

Lillie clapped loudly while her son returned to his seat. "He is making us proud today," she whispered to her husband. Lillie knew changes lay ahead. Edward Jr. had applied at several nursing schools, and so only Katherine would be at home.

That summer Edward Jr. left home for nursing school. He had been accepted into a white school. "I'm proud of you, son," Lillie told him. "I'm so glad you have opportunities your father and I never had." She swallowed a lump in her throat as she watched him drive off. *At least he'll be home every weekend,* she consoled herself, turning back to the house.

One Saturday night at the supper table, Edward Jr. helped himself to a generous helping of mashed potatoes and sausage gravy before passing them to Katherine. "Nobody cooks like you, Mama," he said.

"You're right about that," Daddy Edward said. "It wasn't always that way though." He winked at Lillie.

"Remember how my biscuits were hard lumps instead of fluffy soft ones like Mammaw's?" Lillie smiled sheepishly. "And I was sure I knew just how to make them, but honestly, I don't think Mammaw ever actually showed me how."

Edward turned to his son. "What are they fillin' your head with in college?" he asked.

In spite of the abrupt question, Edward Jr. didn't seem perturbed at his dad's words. "The study is amazing. They teach you everything you need to know about hospitals, nursing homes, and even home nursing."

Katherine laughed. "I'm trying to imagine you working with old people."

"My choice would be a hospital," Edward Jr. said. "I'm afraid, though, my color might make it hard for me to get a job."

Lillie grimaced. Times hadn't changed that much, after all. Her son would still have to deal with prejudice, just like she had. "Just show them what an honest worker you are," she told her son. "That will speak louder than any old color of your face."

"I've applied for some jobs," Edward Jr. said. "But as soon as they see me in person, they change their mind."

"Don't worry, son," Lillie declared. "I'm gonna do some serious prayin'. I'm a-gonna pray you right into that hospital."

"Oh, Mama, your prayers are always chasing me wherever I go." Edward Jr. chuckled.

"Exactly." Lillie nodded decidedly. "That's what powerful prayin' does. Just bitin' at your heels, never letting you rest."

One weekday evening, Edward Jr. called home. "Mama," he said. "I met the most amazing girl here at college. Her name is Isabella."

"Oh?" Lillie exclaimed.

"I'm thinkin' 'bout asking her out. Do you think I should?" Eddie's voice held excitement.

"I don't know, son. I trust your judgement," Lillie said.

"She's a peach," Edward Jr. said admiringly. "She's not a believer like you, Mama, but I think you'll like her."

The next evening, the phone rang again. "Mama?" Eddie couldn't hide his pleasure. "She agreed to go out for milkshakes this evening."

"I'm happy for you, son," Lillie said. "I hope you soon bring her to meet us."

During Christmas vacation, Edward Jr. arrived home from college. "I brought Isabella to meet you," he said proudly.

"So pleased to meet you," Lillie said as she shook the young lady's hand.

The romance progressed quickly, and soon Edward and Lillie were invited to a wedding. Lillie joyfully watched her son walk down the aisle with his beautiful bride.

A year went by. Then two. Edward Jr. had gotten a government job doing water testing. He and his wife purchased a house in Clearmill on Perry Street. Lillie stopped in one Saturday for a visit and found her son out watering his yard and caring for his garden. "You have a lovely place," she told him.

Edward Jr. smiled briefly. "I take pleasure in my beautiful yard, but it's really more than that. Because of other difficult things in my life, it has become an escape, a place where I can go and forget."

"An escape?" Lillie wondered.

"Mama," he said, "Isabella can't have children."

"No shame in that, son. Love her anyway."

"I know, but we both want children so bad it's causing stress in our relationship."

"Oh, Eddie, just keep lovin' her. Remember how your Daddy Edward loved me? Try it on her, and don't make her feel like she is less than a woman by not bearin' you any children."

"She's going back to school," Edward Jr. went on glumly. "I wish she would stay home, but she gets so lonely, maybe it's best."

Not long after, Edward Jr. and Isabella both came to see Lillie. "We are separating for a while," Eddie said. "We just can't make it work."

"I'm sorry to hear that," Lillie said. Her heart ached to think of what her son was going through. She laid a hand on his arm. "Even if you separate, Eddie, it will never make me love you less."

As Lillie sat in the audience at her daughter's college commencement ceremony, she felt the same sense of pride as she had when she watched Edward Jr. walk across the platform.

"These students—the class of '72—have completed the required studies to graduate with a teaching degree," the master of ceremonies announced.

Katherine stood on the platform with her colleagues to receive her diploma. Lillie jumped to her feet, clapping for her daughter. As soon as the ceremony finished, she ran forward and folded her daughter in a big hug. "You have made me so happy," she said. "I love that now both of my children have degrees and both have graduated from white schools. Yay!" She raised her hand in victory.

The next morning, Katherine had more good news. "Mama," she announced, "I just found out I have been hired by the Clearmill Public School."

"Oh, thank you, Lawd!" Lillie said. "My chile is actually one of the first black teachers hired in this town. I'm so happy! Times really are changin'!"

"I think I need to find my own place, Mama. I want to be closer to school," Katherine said.

Lillie's face fell. "I don't like the thought of that."

"But Mama," Katherine pleaded, "it would be so much more practical."

Lillie nodded. "Well, all right then. Let's start house hunting."

Edward and Lillie took their daughter and looked at several small places close to the school where Katherine would be teaching. Finally, they found an apartment Katherine could afford. Lillie helped her daughter pack up her room and move out.

"I ain't gonna know what to do with myself with both my babies gone," she moaned.

"Oh, Mama," Katherine said, chuckling. "I am twenty-two, after all."

"I know. I just hate change," Lillie said. "But I'll be awright."

"You won't sit around and mope all day?" Katherine asked.

" 'Course not. I have my Lawd beside me. We're gettin' along just fine," Lillie said.

One day, Katherine dropped in for a bit. "Guess what, Mama? I've been dating someone special." She waltzed around the room in a circle.

"Who is he?" Lillie asked.

"His name is Mercer. He's such a nice man. Come over to my apartment this evening, and you can meet him."

Lillie stepped into Katherine's apartment, greeted by a beaming Katherine. A handsome young black man casually sauntered up beside her, cocked his head back confidently and surveyed Lillie with half-closed eyes. A contemptuous smirk flitted across his face as he finished looking her up and down. A distinct dislike rose in Lillie, followed by the feeling that she wanted to give this young man a fair chance. Courteously she shook his hand. "Hello," she said. "Katherine invited me to come meet you."

Mercer sniffed. "She told me. Well, hope you like what you see." He guffawed loudly.

After a short conversation, Lillie left quietly. Later that night, the phone rang in Lillie's living room.

"Hello, praise de Lawd!" she answered. It was Katherine, and Lillie could immediately tell she was miffed.

"Mama," she demanded. "What's wrong with Mercer? I don't think you like him."

Lillie sighed. "I don't. Something about him makes me think he's not one of our kind."

"Mama," Katherine said in a scandalized voice. "He's a nice man. He takes me to church and loves me."

"Katherine, I'm gonna tell you one thing, and then I'll shut up. It's better to be alone than married with some people. Some folks come into our lives for a time. Not to stay, but for a season. Are you sure Mercer isn't one of them?"

"Mama, I can't believe you would say that. I love him."

"He's like the leaves of the tree. When the wind blows he goes wherever it takes him. He isn't like the tree that has roots. You need to find a man with roots, and I don't believe Mercer has any."

"Mama!" Katherine cried.

"That's all I wanted to say," Lillie said. She flinched as she heard her daughter slam down the phone at the other end of the line. "Lawd, I'm sorry, but I just have a bad feelin' about this one."

Soon wedding bells were ringing for her daughter. As Lillie turned to watch her daughter walk up the aisle on her daddy's arm, Lillie's eyes misted. "Lawd," she whispered, "let my feelin's be wrong. I want Katherine to be happy."

The reception passed in whirl, and soon the newlyweds were gone. "Edward," Lillie said as they left for home. "I just can't shake the feeling that Mercer ain't all he seems."

"He seems nice to me," her husband said casually. "I think you're worryin' for nothin'."

Lillie couldn't shake the nagging feeling, but she decided to tell her Lord about it.

chapter twenty-two

Sally

"Mama, I want to tell you something," Katherine said one day. "Mercer and I are buying a new house with the money we both saved."

Lillie gasped. "Are you sure you should do that? Why not buy an older house like Eddie did?"

"We want a new house. Mercer said we should go for the best."

"I understand, but maybe you should buy something small and build up your credit before tackling a big payment like that." Lillie's voice expressed her worry.

"Don't worry, Mama. With my teaching job and Mercer's record shop, we shouldn't have any trouble meeting the payment."

Lillie stood stunned. "Record shop? I didn't know anything about that."

"Yes, he opened a record shop in our garage. He sells all kinds of music—Christian, rock, country—he has it all," Katherine said proudly.

"Is it doing well?"

"I–I guess I don't know. He hired his friend to run it, but it seems to be."

"Hired someone? That gets expensive. Does he have any idea what he's getting into?"

"I'm not sure. He doesn't talk to me about that." Katherine's face clouded for a moment.

"Just don't overcommit," Lillie warned.

For the next few years, Mercer and Katherine seemed to be doing well. Lillie tried to lay her doubts to rest.

One evening, they both came home for dinner. "Mama," Katherine said, her eyes shining. "Mercer and I have some exciting news. You and Daddy are going to be a grandma and grandpa."

Lillie clasped her hands. "Praise de Lawd! He's givin' me more than I deserve."

One sunny day, the phone rang. "Grandma, come see little Maria." Mercer's voice rang with pleasure.

"She's here?" Lillie exclaimed.

"Yep. She's a dandy, too," Mercer cooed.

Edward and Lillie hurried to the hospital. Lillie gathered the pink bundle in her arms. Her own granddaughter! Did Pappaw feel as delighted in her as she felt for little Maria? "She's perfect," Lillie told Katherine.

"Isn't she lovely?" Katherine asked.

Lillie gazed into the guileless face of the newborn. "Absolutely!" She suddenly had a strong desire to pass on the same faith to this little one that her grandfather passed on to her.

"Lawd," she prayed aloud, "may this child grow up to love you. May her mama and daddy teach her only what is good. Amen!"

After William joined his sister Maria two years later, Lillie became a full-time nanny to her grandchildren. She told them Bible stories and prayed with them, doing all she could to teach them about God in the few short years she had with them before they headed to school.

"Grandma?" little Maria asked one day. "Mama says these Bible stories aren't true. Is she right?"

Lillie sighed. "How I wish she believed they were true." She hugged her granddaughter close. She knew Katherine might not even like that she filled her children's minds with the Bible, but she determined to keep on until she was prohibited from doing so.

One day, Katherine stopped at Lillie's house. "Mama," she said in a trembling voice, "I wish I would have listened to you way back when you first met Mercer. You said then that something bothered you about him. And you were right. Mercer is lazy, the bills are piling up, and our marriage is in shambles."

Lillie's heart hurt for her daughter. "What about his record shop?"

"He hasn't touched that thing for a long time. I don't think he even knows how to work. They are threatening to close him down if he doesn't pay his bills. Mama, I don't know what to do."

Lillie thought a long time. "I don't think covering his debt will help. He needs to be confronted."

The next day, Katherine called her mother. "He left," she said. Her voice shook. "I have the children. I don't even know if he'll send child support. I'm going to move to Ohio. They need to get far away from their father, and I need a new start."

Lillie's heart hurt for both her children. Neither of them had a marriage that lasted. Was it her fault for not being the mother she should have been?

Katherine called again a day later. "Mama," she said, "I can't take care of my children all alone. What would you think about moving with me to Ohio and being a nanny for my children until I can get my feet on the ground?"

"Well, let me ask the Lawd what I should do," Lillie said. "I'll let you know tomorrow."

The next day, Lillie knocked on Katherine's door. "I'm coming to help you pack. I think God has given me permission to go with you. And," she added uncertainly, "your daddy doesn't care either."

Katherine clasped her hands in front of her. "Oh, Mama, I don't know what I would do without you! It will be easier to settle there with some help from you."

The next week, Lillie and Katherine and her two children packed their car and headed to Ohio. Lillie found a new church there that she liked. She threw herself into life there, first with her grandchildren, and second with the new church she was attending.

Lillie faithfully took her grandchildren to church on Sundays. "Katherine?" she asked before they left one Sunday morning, "are you sure you won't join us?"

Katherine sighed. "I'm too tired to go to church. Just go without me."

Every Sunday, Lillie marched up to the front benches with her charges. Every Sunday she saw the disapproving stare of the pastor. She couldn't understand why he did not approve of her and her grandchildren attending his church. She wondered if he didn't like something about how they were dressed.

After the service one Sunday, the pastor approached her. "Sister Lillie, who are these rebels with you, and why are they dressed like that?"

Lillie's face flushed with anger as she sensed the critical spirit of this man. She had noticed that all the women in the church wore long skirts and long sleeves, but she had hoped they would accept her grandchildren. "These are my dear grandchildren, and I ask that you respect them as you would any person on this earth."

"Are they saved?" the pastor asked.

"No," Lillie answered. "How can they be saved without hearing the truth?"

The pastor cleared his throat. "You can teach them at home."

"That's true, but the Bible says that as the people of God, we are here to draw people to Jesus. How can we do that if you forbid my family to come to church?"

The pastor ignored her question. "There is something else I need to talk to you about. Does your daughter wear pants? If so, you can't live with your daughter and be accepted as a member of this church."

"Pastor," Lillie asked, "where do you find that in the Bible?"

The pastor never answered. Lillie went home from church with a heavy heart.

That night after she tucked the children in bed, she knelt by her bed. "Lawd," Lillie prayed in agony of spirit, "how do I ever teach my family to love you if I can't spend time with them?" She knew she could never obey this unreasonable rule.

The next Sunday, Lillie sat in her pew ready to put her tithe in the offering plate. "Sister Lillie is living in rebellion," the pastor said. "She lives with her family who is not saved. We can't allow this kind of pollution in our church."

Lillie held her tithe money tightly in her hand. "I'm not giving my money to them if they are going to treat me like this," Lillie said to herself. But she knew that wasn't what God was asking her to do, so she gave her tithe anyway.

"I want you to go back to Edward. Katherine will be fine," Lillie heard the Lord telling her.

Lillie didn't want to leave Katherine, but she missed her home in Clearmill. Finally, after much prayer, she decided to move.

Not long after she returned, Edward Jr. called her. "Mama," he said. "I have been single for a long time. I'm lonely and want a wife to share my life with."

"What about Isabella?" Lillie asked. "She's the only one for you, Eddie.

The Bible says it's wrong to have another wife."

Edward Jr. was quiet for a moment. "I can't make it with Isabella, you know that, Mama. I met another woman I want to marry."

"You will be doing that against your parents' wishes," Lillie reminded him. "But of course, we can't make the decision for you."

Edward Jr. married, but he never brought his new wife to see Lillie and Edward. His choices were hard for his parents to accept. With sorrow in her heart, Lillie continued to pray for her children. She believed that her prayers would bear fruit in God's timing.

One evening Lillie picked up the *Clearmill Tribune* lying on the coffee table. She glanced through it quickly. The word "WANTED" caught her attention, and she read the advertisement. "Edward," she said, putting the paper on her lap, "what would you think about taking in some foster children? From this advertisement, it looks like there is a real need. Since Ed and Katherine are gone, I've sometimes wished for some companionship."

"Do we have the love we need to take in underprivileged children?" Ed asked.

"I'll love them with the love of Jesus. What about you?"

"I think I could love them too."

They submitted an application for doing foster care. The approval process, including a home check, moved quickly, and before they could reconsider, Edward and Lillie were approved for foster care. Very shortly after, they received their first foster children. They loved helping needy children, so doing foster care provided them with a way to give. Many children came and went. Would they ever know how they affected the lives of Charles, Becky, Andrew, and Randy? Probably not, but even so, they believed they were doing the right thing. Sometimes, though, even that belief was stretched to the breaking point.

One morning the phone rang. Lillie answered it on the second ring. "Hello, praise de Lawd!" she said, putting the receiver to her ear. She listened a while. "Let me talk to my husband. I'll call you back when we decide, okay?" She hung up the phone. "Ed?" she called.

"What is it?" he asked.

"Social services called and is askin' us if we would take a thirteen-year-old white girl. She is rebellious, and her dad can't handle her. She needs to know who's boss."

Ed smiled. "She would meet her match here."

"You foolin' with me?" she teased, hands on hips.

"Truth hurts," he said, laughing. "Shall we agree?"

"I don't know why not," Lillie said.

The next day, a car drove up, and soon the social worker stood on their doorstep with a girl. "This is Sally," she said when Lillie opened the door.

Lillie gazed at the girl's stony face. Sally stood rigid, fists clenched, as if hoping for a fight. "Hello, Sally."

Silence.

"This is your new home."

Silence again.

"You can call me Granny Clark." Lillie pulled the girl inside. "Now come with me. I'll show you where you will sleep." She led the angry girl down the hall and up the stairs.

Opening the door of Katherine's old room, she paused to let the girl pass into the room. "If you live with me, you will fix your bed," she told the girl bluntly.

"What if I don't?" Sally asked brazenly.

"You don't want to know what I would do," Lillie said darkly, hoping Sally wouldn't challenge her authority.

The next morning, as Lillie fried some eggs for breakfast, the door slammed upstairs. Sally stomped down the stairs. "G'morning," Lillie said, smiling at the new girl.

Sally grunted.

"Look here, young lady!" Lillie dropped her spatula and shook her finger. "When I say 'g'morning,' it means you say it back."

"Morning," Sally muttered.

Lillie put Sally's eggs on a plate and brought them to the table. "Do you want toast or biscuits with your eggs?" she asked.

"Toast," Sally said shortly.

"With butter and jam?"

"Yes."

Sally gobbled her eggs, and then stuffed her toast in her mouth in three massive bites. Lillie bit her lip. *Now's not the time to teach her everything, but she has a lot to learn,* she thought. *She lacks even basic manners.*

While Sally sat in the living room reading a book, Lillie sneaked upstairs to check the girl's room. When she opened the door, her mouth dropped open. A rumpled pile of blankets lay on top of the bed, and clothes were strewn all over the floor.

Realizing she had to win this first battle, Lillie squared her shoulders and headed back downstairs. Without a word, she hauled the girl off the couch and marched her upstairs. "You will fix your bed before you come down for breakfast," Lillie said.

"Dad never made me fix my bed." Sally's voice sounded defiant.

"Maybe he didn't," Lillie said. "But you will while you live here."

Sally yanked the askew blankets and pulled them to cover the bed while Lillie watched her. The look on Sally's face showed Lillie that she may have obeyed outwardly but was still rebelling inside. Lillie didn't press the issue. She didn't want to overwhelm the girl on her first day with them.

The next morning repeated the first. No manners. No niceties. "Sally," Lillie said, "in this house we say 'please' and 'thank you.' I want you to do the same."

"Yes, Granny Clark," Sally mumbled.

Lillie's heart sang. *It's a start. Oh, Lawd, give me wisdom for the next move.*

It seemed Lillie could hardly keep up with the girl. If she wasn't into one thing, she was doing something else she wasn't allowed to do. One day, Lillie realized it was quiet—too quiet. "Sally?" she called. "Where are you?"

She looked upstairs in Sally's room. She wasn't there. She looked in the kitchen and living room. She wasn't there. Had she gone outside? Lillie walked out the door and called again. "Answer me, Sally," she called. No answer.

Lillie walked around the yard, searching high and low. Suddenly she saw shoes dangling from a tree limb. There Lillie found the teen straddling the limbs of the big tree. "Sally," she called. "What are you doing in a tree?"

"Just seeing how it would be to live like a bird."

Lillie smothered a laugh. "Well, you aren't going to be a bird anytime soon."

Sally sighed. "Birds look like they haven't a care in the world. I wanted to be cheerful like them."

"Well, get yerself down from there. Then we can talk about the birds. Besides, it's time you learned to be a lady."

Sally laughed mockingly. "How are you planning to get me down?"

"Get down," Lillie commanded. "You're too old to be climbin' trees."

Sally slowly climbed down, and Lillie brushed off her skirt. "You're gonna ruin every dress you own."

Sally pooched out her lip. "You can't tell me what to do."

"Yes, I can, young lady," Lillie said. Without another word, she led her back to the house. Once inside, Lillie turned to the girl. "So, tell me about the birds, Sally."

Sally hesitated, turning away from Lillie and looking out the window. "Daddy sent me away because I wasn't behaving," she blurted. "I can't do anything right. I looked out my window this morning, and I saw birds in the tree. When I opened the window, they cheerfully sang to me. Granny Clark, I wish I had the life of a bird."

Lillie reached out and squeezed the girl's hand. "Sally," she said, "God loves the birds, but He loves you more. He cares what happens to you. You might not be able to please everyone in your life, but it doesn't mean you are worthless. The birds show us how to be cheerful even when life isn't what we wish it was. Would you really like to be a bird and have to search for food when it becomes scarce?"

Sally shook her head. Lillie didn't push the issue, but got up and went to prepare supper.

That evening after supper, Edward and Lillie relaxed in the living room. Lillie kept a sharp eye on the girl across the room. Sally soon tired of reading and sat on the piano bench and fingered the piano keys. "Do you like music?" Lillie asked.

Sally's eyes lit up for a moment. "Yes."

"Would you like to learn to play?"

Sally nodded. "Oh, I've always liked to sing, and I just know the piano would speak a language I understand."

For the first time, Lillie began to see through a little window into the girl's heart. *I'm going to give that girl music lessons, that's what I'll do,* she decided.

Sally blossomed under her lessons. She practiced tirelessly without Lillie even reminding her. *Maybe this is the key I've been looking for,* thought Lillie.

One evening when Edward came home, Sally was practicing her music. "You will soon be playing like a musician," Edward said.

"Do you really think so, Grampy Clark?" Sally asked.

"Of course, you will. You keep practicin', and soon we will be comin' to hear you at some concert."

For the first time, Sally smiled.

chapter twenty-three

Memories Revisited

From the first week Sally came to live with them, Lillie took her along to church. As the months went by, she saw a desire to know God grow in the girl's heart. One night, Lillie and Sally attended a special meeting at church. As the altar call was given, she watched Sally. Tears coursed down Sally's cheeks, and she stood and walked to the front of the church. "Thank you, Lawd," Lillie said, clasping her hands. But her joy was short lived.

Even though Sally went to church with Lillie and had made a commitment to the Lord, she hung out with the wrong crowd. She danced, drank, and smoked. One evening, Sally went out as she usually did with the church youth group. She wasn't home by curfew, so Lillie drove to where the youth were supposedly having a Bible study. "Sally's not here," one girl told Lillie.

"Where is she?" Lillie asked.

"She never comes here," the girl said. "She lies to you."

Lillie had suspected as much. Not knowing what else to do, she drove back home and waited.

At two o'clock in the morning, a car pulled into the driveway. Lillie cracked open the drapes to see a young man supporting Sally as she staggered into the house. Lillie opened the door. "So this is the thanks I get for taking you in, young lady?"

"Sorrrryyyyy!" Sally stumbled to the couch and slumped down.

Lillie turned to the escort standing in her living room. "And you, young man, are welcome to leave and never return."

"Okay, ma'am." The young man quickly backed out the door, closed it, and ran to the waiting car.

Lillie shook her head as she looked at the form on her couch. The girl snored loudly. Now Lillie knew for sure that Sally was doing things behind her back. Gently, Lillie took off the girl's shoes and pulled a blanket over her. Lillie headed to her room, determined to have a straightforward talk with Sally.

The next morning, Lillie brewed a cup of strong coffee and took the tray to Sally's bedroom. "Good morning," she said as Sally opened one eye. "Time to get up."

"My head hurts," Sally groaned.

"Of course it does. You came in stone drunk last night. Sit up and sip this coffee. It'll help." Lillie helped her sit up. "How long have you been sneaking around with that young man?"

Sally sat in silence.

"I can't force you to do anything, but I don't want you runnin' off. If you stay with me until you're eighteen, I'll give you all the money left over from what I get for taking care of you. You can take it to provide for yourself when you're on your own," Lillie promised.

Sally grunted. "What if I don't?" she muttered.

"It's simple," Lillie said. "You won't get the money. Just remember that."

Lillie could see that for a while Sally tried hard to please her. But soon, the bad habits took over again. Lillie had hoped Sally's improved behavior would last just a few more months until she was eighteen. Then she would be done with foster care and could be independent.

A few weeks before Sally's birthday, Lillie got a phone call. "Hello, praise de Lawd!" Lillie said as she lifted the receiver.

"Granny Clark, this is Sally's mom. I'm coming to get her."

Lillie's heart fell. "I can't refuse, you know that. I'll have her ready," Lillie said in an even voice.

Lillie hung up the receiver. "Sally," she said, turning to the girl sitting at her kitchen table eating her breakfast. "Your mother is coming to pick you up. I made you a promise, and I'll keep it. I'll give you the money."

Sally grinned, eyes lighting up. "But it's not my birthday yet. I'm not the good girl you wish I would be."

"I know that, Sally, but I will bend over backward for you because I love you." Brokenhearted, Lillie reached into her desk drawer where she kept the money for Sally's care. "Here's what I promised you."

Before Sally left with her mother, Lillie gathered the girl in her arms. "Remember, wherever you go, that Granny Clark still loves you."

Sally hugged Lillie tightly. "Granny Clark, I thought this is what I wanted, but now I'm not sure."

Lillie's vision blurred with tears as she watched the car drive out of sight. "Lawd," she reached her hands toward heaven, "go with my girl!" She looked at the house, once again empty of young voices. "I'm gonna miss that little rebel."

Lillie prayed for Sally faithfully.

Several months later, Sally called. "Granny Clark?"

"Hello, Sally! How are you?"

"Fine."

"Are you happy?"

"Yes, Granny Clark," Sally said. As she talked, she tried to cover up her sinful life, but Lillie could see Sally was going downward into her prodigal journey. "Lawd," she prayed. "Don't let her let go of your foundational truths I gave her in my home." Lillie's heart felt peace, even though she grieved over Sally's wrong choices.

With Lillie's grandparents and parents now dead, she began to feel a desire to connect with her roots again. She longed once more to see the plantation where she had lived. She remembered Nora, her cousin in Mississippi whom she hadn't seen since she moved north. She would go find her. Perhaps Nora would treat her with more respect than she had when they were little girls.

Edward took Lillie to the train station in Clearmill and waved her off. "He's a fine man," Lillie murmured to herself as his figure vanished in the distance. She settled into her seat as the train headed toward to Canton. When she arrived in her hometown, she got off the train and headed straight to the hotel for the night. She found a pay phone and called her cousin. "Hello, Nora, it's me, Lillie."

"Lillie? Little Cousin Lillie? Where are you, girl?"

"I'm in a hotel in Canton. I just came by train from Clearmill."

"I'll come get you in the morning," Nora said.

Lillie settled in bed for the night, wondering what memories she would revisit tomorrow.

The next morning, Nora was waiting outside the hotel door with her car. Lillie climbed in. "Where you been?" Nora asked.

"We moved to Clearmill when I was thirteen," Lillie reminded her.

" 'Course, I remember that," Nora said. She wasn't quite as frosty as she had been as a child, but Lillie still didn't feel much warmth from her.

"I am married and have two children. Both of them are living their own lives now, and I decided I wanted to see Canton again."

Nora drove Lillie to the plantation where she grew up. Large shreds of peeled paint hung loosely from the siding of the once-grand house and tall thistles grew up around the shrubbery. Lillie surveyed the property in silence. "Can you drive past my grandparents' place?" she asked finally. "I'd like to see if it's empty."

Nora parked the car in front of the tumbledown shack. Lillie looked at the chipped green paint on the posts on the front porch. "Remember how Pappaw tried to explain why the posts were green?" Lillie asked.

"Yes, I still believe it kept the haunts away."

Lillie walked up slowly and pushed open the front door. *"Crrreeeaaakkk!"* It groaned on its hinges. Lillie pushed the lacy cobwebs aside. The furniture still stood exactly where it had when Lillie lived there. The table was in the same place, the tall poster beds were in their place, and even Mammaw's stove stood in the corner, cold and silent. Lillie blinked back tears. She walked through each room and finally made her way back outside where Nora waited. "I would like to stay here tonight," she said.

"Stay here?" Nora looked astonished. "It hasn't been used in years. Are you sure?"

"Why not? You can even stay with me. There are plenty of empty beds."

Nora locked her car and came inside uncertainly. Lillie hurried outside and gathered a bundle of sticks. Inside she found a yellowed stack of newspaper. She opened the cook stove and piled some twisted paper inside. Laying some small sticks on top, she looked to see if the matches still were where they always were. "Think these will light?" she asked Nora, who was watching.

"It would be a miracle after all these years."

Lillie took one and struck it on the strip. The head fell off. She tried the next one, then the next. They all seemed loath to give her the tiny flame she needed. They lay in a pile on the floor where she had dropped them.

Picking up the last match, she breathed a prayer. "Lawd, please make this one light." She struck it on the side of the box and watched a small flame struggle to burn. Lillie carefully carried it and lit the newspaper in the cook stove. Soon a cheery fire was blazing, and the cabin seemed homey once again.

That night, Lillie lay on the bed she had slept on as a child. The feather tick was gone, but she wrapped up in a blanket Nora had brought in from her car. Even though the bed was hard, she felt quite warm. *I'm glad Nora decided to stay,* she thought as she dropped off to sleep. *I'm not sure if I could have braved the night by myself. Still, it feels good to be close to my roots again.*

The next morning, Nora drove Lillie to town. "I want to show you the Indian reservation near here."

"I'd like that," Lillie replied.

They drove down the highway. Up ahead, Lillie saw a sign that said, "Entering the Choctaw Reservation." Nora drove on like she knew where she was going.

Before long, she pulled up in front of a casino. "I love gambling," Nora said. "I'll get you some lunch here. I love the new slot machines they just came out with. I'll play a few slots while you wait. Maybe today will be my lucky day."

Lillie walked into the restaurant. "You work in this wicked place?" she asked the waiter.

"Lillie, don't say that!" Nora said.

The waiter stood dumbfounded.

"Do you know Jesus?" Lillie asked him.

"Hush!" Nora said. She scooted back her chair, grabbed her purse, and hurried away to gamble her money.

"I wanted to see the reservation, and all she wants to do is gamble," Lillie told the waiter. "Do you gamble?"

He shook his head. "No, I only work here. Now what can I bring you to eat?"

"I'd like some fried chicken and mashed potatoes," she said. "Do you have anything like that?"

"Sure do, ma'am. I'll get that right out to you."

Lillie ate her meal slowly and thought about Nora. *I wonder how she got into gambling. How should I respond?* As the evening wore on, Lillie's heart grew heavier. She wanted to see the Indian reservation, not be cooped up in a casino.

Finally, Lillie saw Nora walking toward her. Her eyes looked sad and her dress hung askew. "Lost it all. Gotta try again tomorrow. Come on, let's go."

That night Lillie sat in Nora's new brick home. "Nora, you've gotten into a bad habit. I want to pray you will be delivered." So Lillie prayed aloud. "Dear Lawd, deliver Nora from the devil of gambling. Make her run far from it and learn to love you. Amen!"

Nora sat in stony silence. "Don't need you to tell me what to do with my life," she said through clenched teeth.

"I won't stop praying for you, Nora." Lillie returned to her room and sorrowfully packed her bags.

The following day, Lillie finished her breakfast before speaking. "I'm leavin'," she said to Nora. "If there is only casinos and gambling left in my family, I see no reason to ever return. I'm goin' home."

Lillie boarded the train with a heavy heart. Mammaw's and Pappaw's faith seemed to have crumbled into oblivion, like the pile of useless matches that Lillie had discarded on the floor of their former home. *Perhaps I can be that last match that still sparks the flame of faith,* Lillie thought as the train rumbled northward.

chapter twenty-four

Shattered Heart

One evening several months after her trip south, Lillie sat in her chair waiting. The clock chimed ten o'clock. "Ed, where are you?" she asked aloud. Just then Lillie jumped as the front door slammed.

"Lillie, I've brought you some flowers."

Lillie smiled. "Ed, you don' need to do that."

Ed cleared his throat nervously. "I needed to," he told her.

The next evening Ed came home with a vacuum cleaner. "I thought maybe you needed a new sweeper," he said, shuffling from one foot to the other.

Lillie looked puzzled. "Ed, I don't need a new sweeper. My old one works just fine. Why are you bringing home so many things?"

Ed shrugged as he walked away. *What's his problem?* Lillie thought. She heard him walk into the living room, sit down on the overstuffed chair, and switch on the television. Knowing he didn't want to be bothered, Lillie went to her room. Opening her Bible, she read a passage before going to bed.

When Lillie woke up during the night, she noticed her husband's side of the bed lay untouched. She got up and went through the house, turning on lights. *Where is that man? Is somethin' wrong?* she worried. She finally opened the door to the spare bedroom. Her husband lay sprawled across the bed, fast asleep. "Ed?" Lillie asked astonishment. "What are you doing in here?"

He rubbed his eyes and sat up. "Aaa-da?"

"Ada?" Lillie gasped. "Who's Ada? This is your wife, Lillie."

He rubbed his eyes again. "Where am I?"

"In the spare bedroom," Lillie said. "And I don't know what you be doing here."

"I didn't want to disturb you when I came to bed, so I just came in here. I hope you don't mind."

Lillie's heart lurched. She turned and went back to her bedroom, where she tossed and turned all night. "Lawd," she prayed, "I dunno what's a going on, but my Ed is not acting himself."

The next morning when Ed came down for breakfast, Lillie had his favorite biscuits and eggs ready for him. He ate in silence. "I need to go," he said, standing up abruptly and grabbing his coat.

"Why, Ed, it's still early. You have an hour yet till your job starts."

"I need to go early, and, oh, I won't be home again till late." He pulled his coat on and hurried out the door without even a kiss.

Lillie stood at the door and watched him go. She rubbed one hand over the other thoughtfully, a perplexed frown creasing her forehead. Something was odd. He had never slept in the spare room before. And why was he leaving early? And why without even a goodbye kiss? Lillie turned to go back in the house, shoulders slumping slightly. *I'll pray,* she thought, pushing away her apprehension. *My Jesus will help me. I'll find out in due time if trouble is comin' my way.*

A week went by. Then a month. One evening, a car pulled into the driveway. Lillie sat at home alone as she often did these days. The door creaked open. "Lillie?"

Lillie jumped at the voice. "Yes, Ed?"

"Come here."

Lillie followed her husband outside. A new red Continental sat in the driveway—a luxury car like she had always wanted. Ed handed the keys to her. "It's for you."

"For me?" Lillie pointed at herself. Then her lips pushed out as her brows came down suspiciously. "Ed, what's your problem?"

"I've never given you any of the things you wanted. You always wanted to live like a rich woman. Now I want you to have this car." Ed smiled weakly.

Lillie raised her eyebrows. "Ed, I've gotten along without a new car all these years. Why now?"

Ed took her hand and kissed it. "I've never been good enough for you."

"Why, Ed, what a thing to say!" Holding the keys in her hand, she walked out to the new car parked in their driveway. She ran her hand over the shiny hood. Her dream car! What was this all about? Ed had been bringing home so many gifts recently. Was he trying to cover up something?

She watched as Ed walked into the house and shut the door. "I have nothing to complain about," she said to herself. Lately she had sensed they didn't have the closeness they once did, but Ed always picked up after himself, fixed his bed, treated her with courtesy, and helped her whenever he could. She knew she had nagged him about keeping the house neat, and she determined again to quit complaining about it.

Lillie tried harder to be a good wife. Before she left for work, she prepared Ed's favorite meal and left a note, telling him where to find it in the fridge. When she arrived home that evening, Ed was filling the sink with water and soap. "Hi," she said, walking in the door.

"Oh, hi," Edward said, putting the dishes in the water and swishing them around.

"How was your supper?"

"Good."

"I made it 'specially for you."

"Thank you," Edward said quietly. "I don't deserve it."

"Edward, of course you do." Lillie's eyes filled with tears. "I may not always tell you, and I nag you more than I should, but you have always been a good husband."

"You have no idea." Edward turned away.

Lillie lay in her bed that night. Sleep would not come. What was wrong with her husband? He seemed so quiet and withdrawn. Frightening possibilities lurked in the corners of Lillie's mind. How could she find out what was really going on? "Lawd," she prayed. "My husband feels like a brick wall. What am I doing wrong? Show me, Lawd!"

A few days later, Lillie heard a knock at her door. She opened it. "Thelma? What brings you here?" She led the way into the living room.

Thelma took off her coat and dropped into a chair. "How've you been? I haven't seen you much since Grapple."

"I know," Lillie said, hanging her head. "You have every right to have rejected me."

"Reject you?" Thelma asked. "What are you talking about?"

"I was a cheat and liar, that's what."

Thelma sighed. "Well, never mind that now. I knew you didn't do that to benefit yourself. You were too honest for that."

"It just got to me when that woman talked about how her husband took all her money and she didn't even have what she needed to live. That would just be awful!"

"I don't think your husband is much different, Lillie. Do you have any idea where your husband goes when he leaves your home?"

Lillie's heart skipped a beat. "W–why, he goes to work, far as I know," she stammered.

"Lillie, I think everyone knows but you. Ed, your dear husband, is seeing another woman."

Lillie's mouth dropped open. "My Ed?"

"Yes," Thelma said.

"I don't believe it." Lillie stiffened in denial, but another part of her wondered if Thelma was right. There were the gifts, the strange hours Ed worked, and the fact that he didn't always come to bed with her anymore.

"It's true. He's in love with your neighbor Ada."

Ada? Ada! Lillie trembled. That's the name Ed had used when she had wakened him that first night when she found him in the spare room. Lillie hardly knew the neighbor lady who had snared her husband. She wanted to deny everything Thelma said, but deep in her heart she knew it was true. Ed had been snatched away from her by a wicked neighbor. "Oh, Thelma, I can't believe this of my Ed. He has never mistreated me. I thought he was faithful."

"Well, think again," Thelma said. "He's been taking her to work every morning for a long time. I'm sorry I had to break the news to you."

"Someone had to," Lillie said woodenly.

"I'm sorry, Lillie," Thelma said, putting her hand on her shoulder.

Thelma closed the door behind her as she left, leaving Lillie dumbfounded on the couch. She buried her head in her hands. "Oh, God," she murmured, "Oh, God, what will I do?"

Immediately she knew. *I'm gonna keep being a good wife to Edward no matter if he's cheatin' on me or not.* She went to the kitchen and made Ed's favorite pie. "Lawd, I'm gonna jes' kill him by bein' a good wife. He will soon be so sorry. Please, help me." Loudly pouring out her grief, she felt upheld by a Power higher than her own.

That evening, Lillie set a piece of pie in front of Edward. Sitting across from him, she nibbled on her own piece. When his plate was scraped clean, Lillie took a deep breath. "I hear you love another woman."

"Who told you that?" Edward's head jerked up angrily.

"Does it matter?" Lillie asked. "The question I want answered is, 'When have I become less than good enough for you?' "

Edward hung his head. "She enticed me, Lillie. I never would have loved her. Please know that I'm a man of my word."

Lillie sniffed. "Then why are you livin' a lie? You give me all these gifts, but behind my back you are seein' another woman!" Lillie felt anger rising within her—ungodly anger. She bit her tongue so she wouldn't say anything she would regret. *I gotta love 'im, even though he's done me wrong! I know I gotta love 'im. But, oh! How I wanna smack 'im in the head right now!* She ground her teeth to keep the bitter words from spewing out.

Edward's eyes flashed. "Keep your nose out of my business! I'm gonna get a divorce in two years." He stomped out, letting the door slam behind him.

Lillie sat at the table for a long time, rocking slightly in her distress. Questions whirled in her mind. *How did we get to this point? Is he really serious about a divorce? Or was it just a threat? And why did he say "in two years"?*

In anguish and confusion, Lillie poured out her heart to God. "Dear God," she prayed. "I'm broken, I'm hurt, and I really don't want to face Edward if he isn't gonna be faithful." As the Spirit of God ministered to her bleeding heart, she felt strengthened. She could go on and continue to love her husband. With God's help, she would even try to love the woman who had stolen his heart. Peace returned.

That night Edward came home late again. Lillie closed her Bible as he cleared his throat to speak. "I'm going to move my things into the spare bedroom upstairs."

Lillie wanted to tell him his announcement was just a formality, since they hadn't been sleeping together much recently anyway. But she didn't. "As you wish," she said simply.

Ed tromped upstairs, and Lillie could hear him moving things around. He came downstairs, and sheepishly cleared his throat, "I shouldn't ask this, I know, but could you help me? I'm not sure what needs to be moved out."

Lillie wanted to shout, "Everything!" But she bit her tongue. "I'll do it tomorrow," she said.

The following day after Ed left for work, Lillie filled her arms with his clothes and carried them to the spare bedroom. Carefully she folded each one and laid them in the empty dresser drawer. "You will always be my husband," she said aloud, "no matter how much you hurt me."

She hugged his shirts to herself as she hauled them on hangers across the hall to hang in the closet. "Oh, my Jesus, clothe that man with humility!" she prayed earnestly. She put his shoes side by side on the floor. "Lawd, make his feet hurt when he walks in wicked ways." Her voice lifted loud and strong as she did battle with the devil over the soul of her wayward husband.

Then she slowly walked back to her room. How cold and bare it seemed without Ed's things! Her heart squeezed as she thought about the lonely years ahead. "Ed, I never imagined our marriage would end like this," she sobbed, sitting down on the bed. Her shoulders heaved and her work-worn hands pressed down hard on her knees. "I thought we had a good relationship." Her mind swirled with questions and confusion.

Ed came in late again that evening. This time, he didn't even speak to Lillie before going to his room. The floor squeaked overhead as he walked. As tears threatened again, Lillie turned her heart toward God and again felt herself enveloped in warmth as she laid her burden at the feet of her Father.

chapter twenty-five

Crisis

Lillie lifted her coffee cup and stole a glance at Edward across the breakfast table. He was deeply engrossed in his newspaper as usual. She had done a lot of thinking since finding out about Ed's affair a few weeks ago, and she had made up her mind. Taking a deep breath, she gathered her courage and blurted, "I'm goin' with you, Edward. Every mornin' you leave so early, and I want to see what you are doin'."

Edward shook his head, but kept his eyes on his paper. "No, Lillie, you don't want to do that."

"Oh, yes, I do, and you daren't tell me I can't."

"I don't want you along, Lillie. You will just be hurt."

"I will go." Lillie's chin jutted out firmly. She gathered her purse and the things she would need for the day and stood by the door, challenging him with her eyes.

Edward said no more. Lillie followed him out the door and down the street to Ada's house. She waited while he knocked, and soon Ada came out, laughing and smiling. She halted with a jerk when she saw Lillie waiting. After a quick, questioning glance at Edward, she tossed a hateful look at Lillie, then took Edward's arm and waltzed down the street beside him. Lillie followed, pain and anger searing her heart. "Lawd," she prayed. "Give me love for this woman who is enticing my husband."

Edward walked Ada to work. "Goodbye, love," Ada cooed as he kissed her.

"Goodbye," he said uncomfortably, then turned and walked with Lillie to the house she was cleaning that day.

How Lillie wished he would give her the same tender treatment, but instead, he left her at the door without a word. Lillie stomped into the house, slapped her purse down beside the door, and hurried to find the dust cloth and mop. She cleaned furiously, muttering to herself all the time. If she didn't do something with her emotions, she just might hurt someone. Her emotions calmed considerably by the time she was ready to polish the silverware. Rubbing the knives and forks gave her time to think and remember how faithful God had been. "Oh, God, I bring my anger to you," Lillie whispered. Once again, God ministered to her wounded heart.

That evening, Lillie felt calm as she walked home. She greeted Edward as if nothing had happened. Lillie knew now that she would find God's grace sufficient, just like the Bible promised.

Several mornings later, Lillie's doorbell rang. She hurried to answer it. "Hello?" she said to the stranger standing on the porch. "Do I know you?"

"Don't you recognize me, Granny Clark?"

Lillie looked closer. The voice seemed familiar. Suddenly she knew. "Sally? Is it truly my dear Sally? Come in, dear, and let's catch up." She pulled the young woman into a deep embrace before leading her into the house.

Sally sat down on the couch and took off her coat, laying it beside her. "Granny Clark, you look sad. What's wrong?"

"I don't want to talk about me, I want to hear about you," Lillie insisted.

"I've missed you so much since you left my home so abruptly that day so many years ago."

"No, Granny Clark, God has led me to you. Please share with me what's wrong. I'm here, and I plan to stay awhile. I missed out on so many years with you."

Lillie sat down beside her. "God bless you, child. My heart broke when you left, but now I see God has answered my prayers for you."

"Indeed He has, Granny Clark," Sally said. "He's been so good to me. Now tell me what's going on."

Lillie took a deep breath. "I wish I could say that everything is fine, but it isn't. I had been suspicious somethin' was wrong with Edward for a while, but I didn't know what. Finally, I discovered he had fallen in love with another woman. She just lives down the street a piece. It broke my heart."

Sally pulled her close. "Oh, Granny Clark! My heart is breaking with yours. I think you need someone to minister to your needs. You gave me so much, it's time I repaid my debt. Do you mind if I stay for a few days?"

"Of course not, dear," Lillie said. "Make yourself at home."

Sally put her things in her old bedroom and soon joined Lillie in the kitchen. "Now you sit down," Sally said. "I'm brewing you some peppermint tea."

Lillie leaned on the table and closed her eyes. It felt good to let someone else take care of her. Sally set a steaming china tea cup in front of her. Sally had picked out Lillie's favorite cup—the one with delicate vining roses and a gold-colored gilt edge. "Aw, Sally, you're spoilin' me already," Lillie said.

Sally sat across from her and lifted her own cup of tea. Steam curled around her face. "Granny Clark, you were right those many years ago. How I wish I had listened to you! I could have saved myself so much heartache."

Lillie reached over and laid her wrinkled black hand on the slender white one. "God redeems all our mistakes. It does my old colored heart good to see you happy and servin' the Lawd."

"I broke off from that boy soon after I left your place. All he wanted was to get me drunk, but in my heart I wanted a better life than that. I've always been sorry I ran out on you. God got a hold of my life and brought me a wonderful Christian husband and three darling children."

Lillie raised her arms toward heaven. "Praise de Lawd!"

Sally's face was full of emotion. "I have you to thank, Granny Clark. I will bring my family to see you someday."

"Please do," Lillie said. "I would love to meet my grandchildren."

But even the comfort of Sally's care could not mend the shreds of Lillie's heart.

Years passed. Lillie, in her upper sixties by this time, kept turning to God for solace as daily she faced the deep pain of her husband's infidelity. One morning, Lillie heard a noise on her front porch. She hurried to her front door. Opening it, she saw a woman weeping. "Ada!" She recoiled instinctively from the woman who had snared her husband. "What's wrong?"

"Lillie," she cried, "you gotta come with me. Something's wrong with Edward. He's not right."

Lillie took a deep breath. Wouldn't it serve him right if he got sick at Ada's? She put her coat on and followed Ada to her house. She had never entered Ada's home before and wondered how she would feel and what she would find. She opened the door. Cheerful pottery lined the window sills. Lillie knew Ada made pottery, but she never dreamed it would be so pretty. The house looked well-kept and homey. *What was I expecting anyway?* Lillie thought. *Some dark, dismal cave?*

"Hurry," Ada said. "Edward really needs you."

Lillie took a deep breath and followed Ada into her bedroom. Edward lay on the bed, moaning. "Edward?" Lillie asked. "What's wrong?"

Edward mumbled something, then Lillie noticed his arm hanging limply by his side. His face drew to the left. She recognized an emergency. "Ada," she said, "we need to get him to the hospital. I think he's had a stroke."

Ada wrung her hands. "I don't know how."

"Where's your phone?" Lillie asked. "I'll call my son."

Ada led her to the kitchen.

Lillie quickly dialed her son's number. "Can you come?" Lillie asked when Edward Jr. answered. "I'm here at our neighbor's place."

Within minutes, Edward Jr. pulled up in his car and hurried into the house. "Mama?" he asked. "What are you doin' over here? What's wrong?"

"It's your father," she said. "We need to get him some help. I need you to lift him and bring him downstairs." She had managed to keep Edward's horrible secret from Edward Jr. and Katherine, but now she knew they would ask questions. She led him upstairs and into the room where his father lay.

"Dad," he whispered, "we're gonna get you to see a doctor." Without asking any questions, he laid the limp arm over his body and lifted his father gently. He carried him downstairs and out the door to where he had parked his car. "Help me get him in the back, Mama."

Lillie got in the passenger seat beside her son. She glanced out the window as they sped away. Ada stood in front of her house, still wringing her hands. *What a cream puff!* Lillie thought. *Calling me in an emergency indeed! Why didn't she care for Edward when he was sick if she was gonna take him when he was well?*

Lillie turned her attention to the man on the seat behind her. After all, he was her husband, and she knew God asked her to care for him till death. "Ed," she whispered, reaching back to rub his arm, "we are takin' you to the hospital so they can make you better. Somethin' ain't right."

Edward mumbled again. Lillie pinched her eyes shut and breathed in deeply. *I'm not going to cry now. I need to be strong for Edward. How can I bear to watch my big strong husband be helpless and weak?* A deep love for her husband washed over her—a love she knew was the love of Christ.

chapter twenty-six

Loving Through Heartache

At the hospital, the nurses whisked Edward off for tests. Lillie and Edward Jr. sat side by side in the waiting room. "Mom," Edward Jr. turned toward her, consternation lining his face. "What was Dad doin' in that woman's house anyway?"

Lillie sighed, and her eyes filled with tears. "I didn't want you children to find out, but your father has been . . . well, been seein' Ada for a long time. He lives at home, but we have separate bedrooms. It's the hardest thing I've ever experienced, but God has helped me forgive." Her voice broke. "My Lawd is helpin' me love your daddy, even though he's wronged me," she whispered.

"Mom!" Edward Jr. shouted, his face dark. "How could he mistreat you like that? I hate him for this!"

"That isn't Jesus' way, Eddie," Lillie said, using his boyish name. "God has ministered to my broken heart so many times."

Edward Jr. said nothing, but Lillie saw him clench his fist. She reached over and put her hand on his. "I know it hurts, Eddie, after the fallout you had with Isabella. But hard as it is, I want you to know, I forgive your father. I will care for him if I must because I promised him so many years ago that I would."

Edward Jr. put his arm around Lillie's shoulders. "I'll help you, Mom," he said in a husky voice. "I want to forgive him too. To not forgive only makes a person bitter."

"Eddie?" Lillie asked. "I haven't asked you recently, but have you ever thought about givin' your heart to God?"

Edward Jr. was quiet for a long time. "Yes, Mama, I have, but I'm not sure I'm ready yet."

"Let the Lawd speak, son. In His time He will draw you. I feel it."

Lillie sat quietly by her son, staring out the window. The sun was setting over the town. Lillie could feel God speaking peace to her spirit again. Soon the door opened, and the doctor came out. "Mrs. Clark?"

"Yes, Doc?"

"Your husband had a stroke, and his left side is experiencing some paralysis. We want to keep him here for observation. Hopefully, we can eventually transition him to the nursing home."

"I'll care for him," Lillie responded quickly. "I'll take him home. My son will help me. Please let us take him home."

The doctor gave a lopsided smile. "He could very well be helpless, you understand. He will need help with all his needs."

"I understand," Lillie said.

"You're sure a plucky woman," the doctor said. "I think he would get good care in your hands, but I'm afraid I must put him in a nursing home."

"Can we see him, Doc?" Lillie asked.

"Yes, follow me." The doctor led the way down the sterile hall to Edward's room.

Edward opened his eyes when Lillie walked in. She went to his bedside and took his good hand. He gripped it tightly and mumbled something, but Lillie couldn't understand a word.

"Don't talk now, Edward," she whispered. "We'll talk when you get better." She stroked his hand lovingly until he relaxed and fell asleep.

Every day, Lillie went to the hospital. Edward improved so slowly that Lillie wondered if he would ever be able to talk again. "Edward," she said as she sat there one day, "I asked my minister to come see you. You don't mind, do you?"

Edward squeezed her hand again. Lillie hoped that meant yes. How she longed for Edward to accept Jesus as his personal Savior while he still had a sound mind.

The next morning, Brother Smith stopped by and read a passage of Scripture. "That blesses my heart," Lillie told him. "And Edward thanks you for comin' too."

Every day, Lillie's minister dropped in and read a chapter aloud in Edward's room. It blessed Lillie to have the support of her church leader. Lillie could tell her husband was listening, but he hadn't been able to say anything understandable yet.

One morning, Edward seemed restless. Lillie stepped close to his bed and took his hand. "What is it, Edward?"

"Dir . . . mmm," Edward mumbled.

"Try again," Lillie encouraged. "You can do it."

With all his effort, Edward tried again. "Dirr . . . ty," he panted.

"Dirty?" Lillie asked. "Is that what you said?"

Edward squeezed her hand. Lillie thought she saw a slight nod. "Can you try again tomorrow?" Lillie asked, confused.

Another squeeze.

The next morning, Lillie arrived early. She didn't want to miss a chance to communicate with Edward if he tried to say something again. "Good mornin', Edward," she said as she came into his room. "How are you this mornin'?"

He squeezed her hand.

"Did you sleep well?"

He squeezed her hand again. Then his head shook from side to side.

"Did you want to tell me somethin'?"

He squeezed her hand again. Lillie waited.

"Did dir–ty," he mumbled.

"You did me dirty?"

Edward squeezed her hand and nodded slightly.

"Sorrr–y," he tried again.

"Are you saying you are sorry that you did me dirty?"

Edward's head nodded.

"I forgive you, Edward."

He squeezed her hand again as two tears slowly slid down his cheek. Lillie took a cloth and wiped them gently. She noticed some patches of gray in his tightly curled hair. *He's still the most handsome man I ever met,* she thought. *Oh, Ed, if only you would have come to God much earlier in life. We would have grown old happily together.*

The minister continued his daily visits, reading Scripture to Edward each time. Lillie watched her husband closely. He listened attentively to each word. Over time, his speaking slowly improved.

"Did you enjoy the Scripture reading today?" Lillie asked.

"Y–y–eee–sh!" Edward said.

"Good morning," Ada called one morning, announcing her presence at the open door of Edward's room. Her high-heeled shoes clicked across the floor as she walked toward his bed. She wore a smart-looking navy blue blazer and matching slacks, and her hands clutched a vase of flowers. "How are you?" she asked brightly.

"Better!" Edward said.

"Get well soon," Ada chirped. Her perkiness struck a false note with Lillie. Nervously Ada set the bouquet on the windowsill and whirled around to leave. Lillie could tell Ada was repulsed by the atmosphere of illness. She followed her neighbor out into the hall.

"Ed is doing better," Lillie said. "His speech is comin' back, and I hope we can soon take him home."

Ada nodded carelessly. "That's nice. I guess you'll have to take care of 'im though, because I don't have anything but an upstairs bedroom for him."

Lillie took a deep breath. "You've ruined our marriage, Ada. You have cheated me of my husband. But my Lawd has ministered to my hurt, and I cannot leave Edward without care. If you aren't gonna help him, I will."

"I can't stand to see him this way," Ada spit out. She turned and rushed out the front door. *The poor woman doesn't know what commitment really is!* Lillie thought.

After what seemed like a long time, the doctor gave permission for Edward to be transferred to a local nursing home. Lillie helped him settle into his new room. She smoothed his bed, opened the drapes, and put a fresh bouquet of red roses on the bedside table. "I wish I could stay with you, Ed," Lillie said, "but it's against policy. I will come every day."

Ed nodded. Before she left him for the night, she helped him from his wheelchair into his bed.

Lillie quit her job so she could care for her husband. She patiently fed him lunch and supper before going home for the night.

"H–hom–mme!" Ed said one day when Lillie pushed open his door.

"You want to go home, don't you?"

Edward nodded.

"I'll see what I can do," she said. Then suddenly she grew cold. Did Ed want to go to her house or Ada's? She didn't want to upset him by asking him. She would assume he was talking about her home.

Ed continued to improve. One weekend Lillie got permission to take him home for the weekend. She called Edward Jr. "Could you come and help me take your daddy home for the weekend? The doctor gave me permission, but I don't think I can do it myself."

Edward Jr. arrived that evening after work. "Daddy?" He bent down and kissed his father's forehead. "You're looking spry tonight. Are you ready to go home with Mama?"

Edward nodded. Lillie sighed with relief. He never mentioned Ada as Eddie pushed the wheelchair out and helped his father into the car, nor when they drove to Lillie's house.

Edward's eyes brightened during the drive. Many weeks had passed since he had seen sunshine and green grass.

"It–it's nice," Edward said as they drove up in front of their home.

"You're glad to be home, aren't you?" Lillie asked.

"Ye–es," he said slowly.

Lillie sighed with relief. Now she knew she had brought him to the right place.

Lillie and Edward Jr. wheeled him into the house. Edward Jr. carried him up the stairs to Lillie's bedroom. She wanted him close so she could care for him better. They hadn't been in that room together since she had found out about his sin. Lillie watched Edward's face. A lonely tear slid down his cheek. She stroked his dusky hand. "It's all forgiven," she said huskily. Compassion for her husband filled her heart as she ministered to his physical needs.

Ed relaxed during the weekend home. "I–I w–wanttt s–stay," he stammered on Sunday evening.

Lillie squeezed his hand, and tears clouded her eyes. "I can't handle you by myself, or I would, Ed. Do you believe me?"

He sighed and nodded. Lillie could see he had resigned himself to returning to the nursing home.

The minister continued to visit him at the nursing home. "Edward," he asked one day, "would you like to give your heart to the Lord?"

Edward sat quietly for a long time. "M–my wife is Chris–tian. I d–don't des–serve for–give–ness." The sentence wore him out.

Lillie laid her hand on his. "All have sinned and come short of the glory of God. You can be forgiven now, Edward."

Tears trickled down his dark cheeks. The minister led in prayer, and Lillie prayed. Edward's face glowed when they finished. "H–happ–py!" he said.

Lillie took his hand again. God had answered her prayers! Ed's salvation had come to pass, but not in the way she thought it would. *God's plan is so much higher than ours,* she thought.

Going to the nursing home to see Edward every day during the week and bringing him home on the weekends required a lot of energy and sacrifice on Lillie's part. "Lawd, you're gonna have to give me strength for this job you have asked me to do," she prayed.

Edward's speech returned to almost normal. "I h–hate how hard you have to w–work to help m–me, Lillie. You can't imagine how h–helpless it makes a m–man feel to not be able to do th–things for himself."

Lillie's heart ached with compassion for her husband. "I would do any-thing for you, Edward, and I promised to love and care for you until death parts us. God never told us what that would be."

Edward's head slumped. "I–I w–wish I c–c–could do it o–over again."

Lillie stroked his hands and kneaded his shoulders. "Let's just enjoy the time we have left and shut those regrets behind a big ol' metal door." He drew her to himself with his one good arm. She leaned her head on his shoulder, glad for this moment of intimacy they hadn't experienced in years.

chapter twenty-seven

Love Triumphs

Lillie cherished the time they had together after Edward surrendered to Christ. Evenings together at the nursing home she read books to him and helped him put puzzles together. Sometimes they just talked. One evening, Ed seemed to have something on his mind. "At night, I see visions of h–heaven, Lillie. It's so b–beautiful and inviting. All I w–want to do is go th–there."

"Please stay with me a bit longer, Edward," Lillie begged. "I need to go home tonight. I will be back first thing tomorrow mornin'."

Lillie hesitated to go home. She worried Edward might need her during the night. But she also knew she needed her sleep to keep taking care of him.

The next day Lillie asked, "Would you like me to take you to church?"

"Yes–s–s!" Edward's eyes lit up.

The following Sunday, Lillie drove Edward to her church. She struggled to push his wheelchair through the gravel to the church house, but his joy more than repaid her for the trouble of getting him there. "I w–want to be baptized," he told her after the service. "J–just like y–you were so m–many years ago."

Lillie talked to the ministers. They agreed to baptize him the next Sunday. Lillie's face shone when she wheeled him to the same pool where she had been baptized years before.

"I baptize you in the name of the Father, Son, and the Holy Ghost," the minister said. Because Ed used a wheelchair, they poured the water over his head.

Even though his face sagged, his arm still hung limp, and he couldn't leave his wheelchair, Ed's face glowed with his newfound faith in God. *Is this the same man I married?* Lillie wondered as she gazed at his transformed face. She felt a tender love for him she had never experienced before. *Dear Edward. How glad I am that God gave him a second chance!*

After Lillie tucked him into his bed in his room at the nursing home, she followed the nurse out to the nursing station. "He's a changed man," the nurse said. "Something's got a hold of him. He doesn't smoke cigarettes or swear at us anymore."

"It's God, glory hallelujah! He is in the changin' business. Wouldn't you like to experience it too?"

The woman chuckled. "If it would change me like it changed him, maybe I should try it."

"You should," Lillie said. "Please let me pray for you."

"Go ahead and pray, but I need to think about this first. I'm not ready to make a commitment today."

" 'To day if you will hear his voice, harden not your hearts,' "[1] Lillie quoted. "You might not have tomorrow."

"I'll think on it," she said.

That night, Lillie called her daughter. "I think you should come see your daddy," she said. "He's a changed man."

The next day, Katherine drove to Clearmill to see her daddy. Lillie's foster daughter Sally and Edward Jr. came too. Right there in that room at the nursing home they had a little family reunion.

"Children, I w–want to t–tell you s–something," Edward said in his simple way. "Your mama was r–right all these y–years. I was w–wrong. I wish I had accepted God m–many y–years ago like y–your mama w–wanted me to."

Edward Jr. took his father's hand. "I see somethin' has changed you, Dad. I will be thinkin' on it."

They settled him in his bed and walked out into the hall together. "I see such a light in his eyes," Sally said. "God asked you to care for him and you did. Granny Clark, you are such an inspiration to me."

Katherine looked away. She slipped on her jacket and turned to leave. Lillie followed her down the hall to the front door. "Mama, it's hard to see Daddy like this." Katherine's eyes filled with tears.

"I know, darlin', but he needs us even more now than he ever did. Do you realize how helpless he feels?"

Katherine sighed. "Eddie told me how Daddy got another girlfriend and wasn't true to you. That makes me feel so angry toward him."

"I know it does, dear," Lillie said. "But I've forgiven him, and I know God has too. Your daddy has such visions of heaven that sometimes I feel like I want to leave this ol' earth right now. I hope you can find it in your heart to forgive him too."

"I don't want to, Mama Lillie," she said bitterly.

"I can't force you to, Katherine," Lillie said. "But I'm prayin' you will. And he hasn't once asked about Ada since he had his stroke. I think he wants to show me he is sorry."

That night, Lillie sat a bit longer than usual with Edward. "I feel like our time together might be short," she said.

He nodded. "I'm ready to go h–home. I'm tired of my b–body that doesn't f–function right anymore. But, Lillie, I have one r–request of y–you."

"What is it, Ed?"

"I'm afraid y–you will be a–angry when I tell you my h–heart. Even though I was wrong in l–loving Ada the way I did, I still can't help but feel s–some responsibility for h–her. Do you understand what I m–mean, Lillie?"

Lillie felt jealousy rising within her, but she prayed silently for compassion. "I think I can a little bit, Ed, even though it puts a knife to my heart when you mention her name."

Ed rubbed a tear from his eye. "I h–have no right to ask this of you, L–Lillie. I know I don't. B–but I have one request to m–make before I d–die."

"What is it, Ed?" Lillie's blood chilled as she waited for his request.

"I'm a–ashamed to even ask, but w–would you promise to care for A–Ada after I'm g–gone? She h–has no one, you know."

Lillie's breath left her. The room swam around her for a moment. *Help me, Jesus!* her heart cried out. *I'm needin' you bad now!* She swallowed hard. "This is the hardest promise I ever made, but if that is your wish, I will honor you by carin' for her."

Ed squeezed her hand. "I d–do want you to know I l–love you. And th–thank you for showing me your J–Jesus."

For a long while Lillie sat holding his hand. Finally she knew she must tear herself away from his side so he could get his rest. "Good night, Love!" she said as she stood up. "I need to go home." She tucked the blankets around him.

"Good n–night!" Ed reached his good arm up and pulled her close. She kissed him gently. Softly she closed the door behind her as she left.

The next morning, her telephone rang. "Your husband passed away during the night," a nurse from the home said gently. "Please accept our deepest sympathies."

Even though she had mentally prepared for this moment, the news still shocked her. Edward was gone! She was a widow at sixty-one years old.

Lillie leaned on the table and cried for the wasted years of sin that Edward had lived, for the pain he had caused her when he started loving another woman, and for the promise she had made before he died! How would she ever find the grace to carry on?

Her tears of sorrow turned to tears of joy when she thought of how Ed had given his life to Christ. Because of that, they had experienced reconciliation before his death. She thanked God for the love she carried in her heart for her deceased husband.

The funeral was simple. Lillie knew Edward had requested songs about heaven, so she chose some of his favorite ones. Katherine and Edward Jr. and Sally joined her in front of the casket as they viewed their father and husband for the last time. "He loved you all dearly," Lillie whispered. "And he was a good dad." They wiped their eyes and waited to follow the casket to the cemetery. Ada followed at a respectable distance behind them all the way. Lillie tried not to think about the awkward situation but rather focused on her own loss of losing her life companion.

Edward Jr. came to see her soon after the funeral. "Mama," he said, "what are you going to do about Ada? I think you should go confront her about her terrible sin."

"What good would it do?" Lillie asked. "Your daddy is gone, and before he died, he repented of his sin. I don't want to bring up the past."

But one night, Lillie got a call from Ada's daughter. "Can you come see my mom at the hospital? She is very sick and is asking for you."

"Why me?" she mumbled aloud to herself as she hung up the phone.

A voice whispered insidiously inside her, "She didn't even ask you to forgive her. Why would you care about her?"

"I care about her because she has a soul," Lillie said aloud. Determined to help, Lillie drove to the hospital. Walking down the familiar hall, she read the numbers on the doors. Finally, she reached Ada's room and knocked on the door. She heard a voice call weakly, "Who is it?"

"It's Lillie Clark." Lillie stepped inside without waiting for an answer.

"And what is your motive?" Ada asked suspiciously.

"To tell you about Jesus," Lillie said firmly. She sat down beside the sick woman and took her hand. She began to pray. "Lawd, heal my neighbor Ada. Show her sins to her and help her to repent."

Ada's eyes filled with tears. "I took your man, and now you come an' pray with me?" She turned her face away. "I can't look at you. You're a true Christian."

"We all have sinned, Ada," Lillie said. "But God's grace is there for us. Edward is gone. I want God to save your soul. Won't you think about acceptin' Him while you still have opportunity?"

Ada was quiet a long time. "The doctors told me I have cancer, and they don't expect me to live long." Her voice faltered to a stop. "I'll think about it. Come back tomorrow, and we'll talk some more."

"Can I bring a minister with me tomorrow?"

"Yes. I would like that."

The next morning, Lillie brought her minister to see Ada. He read Scripture to her and prayed for her. Lillie prayed too.

"Thank you," Ada choked out as they were leaving. "You don't know how much it means to me to have you come in here."

Lillie and her minister visited Ada every day. One day, Ada's daughter followed them out into the hall and shut the door. "The doctor says Mama has improved enough that we can take her home soon."

"Well, glory be!" Lillie cried. "The Lawd is givin' her one more chance."

The following week, Ada returned home. Lillie visited her every day, taking her soup so she could get her strength back. Every day, Lillie asked her about her soul.

Finally, after many weeks, Ada yielded. She wept loudly and started repenting. She called on Jesus' name. "Lawd, save me from my sins," Ada prayed. "Lawd knows I've been wrong."

Then Lillie prayed. "Thank you, Lawd, for your convicting voice. Please hear Ada's prayer."

"Oh, Lillie." Ada's tears choked her voice so she could barely speak. "What I did was so wrong. It was inexcusable to take another woman's husband. Oh, won't you forgive me?"

Lillie's eyes moistened. "Of course, I forgive you."

"I did you so dirty, and now you're so nice to me."

Lillie took her hand. "That's only the grace of my good Lawd that gave me love for you."

As Lillie walked down the street to her own home, she felt the Lord's presence with her. Again, her spirit felt lifted above herself. Uncaring of the sidelong looks cast her way, she lifted her hands in praise and shouted glory to God. She knew Jesus would be with her as she ministered to her late husband's mistress.

chapter twenty-eight

Life as a Nanny

The next day Ada asked Lillie to come see her again. "I have things I must return to you," she said. "I got a boat, money, and some other things Edward gave me. I wanna return them."

They walked outside to see the luxurious boat sitting beside the garage. "But you will have nothin' left if you give this to me," Lillie said.

"I know, but these things aren't mine. They're yours."

Lillie felt a stab of pain as she thought about how Edward's guilt drove him to shower both of his women with gifts to keep them happy. Poor Edward. In trying to live a double life, he had made himself miserable for so many years.

What should she do with all these extravagant things? "Sell the boat," a still, small voice told her. "Give Ada the money. It would provide for her for a long time."

Lillie found a buyer for the boat and the many other things Edward had given Ada. Looking at the money in her hand, that smooth, insidious voice whispered again. *You don't have to give it to Ada. No one would ever know. After all, that woman sinned with your husband; why should you reward her for it?*

"Get behind me, you slippery ol' devil!" Lillie spoke firmly to dispel the tempter's voice. "I promised Edward I would care for Ada, and that's jes' what I'm gonna do. Besides," Lillie smiled to herself, "Pappaw always told me we had to love folks even when they do us dirty." Her smile vanished. "And I'm guessin' that was about as dirty as it's gonna get."

Taking the money, she went to see Ada again. "I want you to have this money," she said. "Before he died, Edward asked if I would care for you. I sold the boat, and now I want you to keep this money so you can care for yourself."

Ada's eyes filled with tears again. "Truly you are a woman of God."

Through Lillie's daily visits and compassionate care, she and Ada became good friends. Both lived alone now, so they spent time together, and Lillie even asked Ada if she would teach her to do pottery.

"Of course I will," Ada said. "You just come over tomorrow, and we'll make some together."

The next morning, Lillie watched as Ada pumped the wheel with her feet. She took a blob of gray clay and began forming it with her hands. As the wheel spun, she applied water to keep the clay moist and maintained constant pressure at just the right spots. A beautiful vase took shape beneath her touch.

Lillie watched, amazed. "You make it look so easy."

Ada laughed. "It is. Here, you try it with this piece."

Lillie took the clay and put it in the middle of the wheel and began to pump with her feet. The clay began to spread. She tried to add water and shape it as Ada had, but soon the lump turned out misshapen and ugly.

Ada patiently took Lillie's clay and started over. Soon the ugly clay had been formed into a bowl. Then Ada coated both pieces with a solution and put them in the kiln on high heat. As the pieces baked, the clay dried and the glaze shone and stuck to the pottery. "You indeed have a talent," Lillie told Ada that night. "I could never do anything like that."

"It just takes practice," Ada told her. "You can try again another day."

Lillie smiled. "We'll see. Did you know the Bible likens us to lumps of clay in Jesus' hands?"

"Really?" Ada asked. "I can understand that word picture very well since I do pottery. We are indeed only clay waiting to be formed by Him. I love that thought."

Lillie and Ada started going to church together during the next year. Soon Ada wanted to be baptized. Lillie's heart swelled with happiness. Now they were truly sisters in Christ!

Day by day, Lillie noticed Ada getting physically weaker. One morning Lillie took her friend some tea when she went to Ada's house for her daily visit. "Ada," Lillie said, "drink tea with me. It will give you strength."

Ada obediently took the china tea cup and drank tea with Lillie. "You treat me so well. What would I ever do without you?"

Lillie smiled. "I brought some soup for your supper too. Friends help friends. With God bindin' us together, I want to spend all the time together we can."

"Lillie." Ada carefully focused on turning the cup in its saucer. "Sometimes I'm afraid."

"What are you afraid of?"

"That because of my life of sin, God somehow won't accept me when I die." Her voice came as a thread of sound.

Lillie took her hand. "Didn't you give your heart to God and confess all the sins in your past?"

Ada nodded.

"Don't let ol' Satan come in and stomp on your peace. God saved you. You gotta hang on tight to that promise."

The day came when Ada wouldn't even try to get out of bed. Ada's daughter called again. "Lillie, Mama is very low. Can you come?"

Lillie dropped everything and went to Ada's house immediately. Ada lay on her bed with eyes closed and face slackened. Her breathing was slow and ragged. Lillie leaned over the bed and took her friend's hand. "Ada, I remind you, you are a child of God. Don't let that ol' deceiver give you any doubts. You have asked forgiveness for all your sins. You can leave here in peace. I love you."

Lillie felt the hand relax. She looked at Ada's daughter. "I think she's gone," she said simply.

"Oh, Mama!" Ada's daughter dropped to her knees beside the bed and took her mama's lifeless hand in hers.

Wiping her own tears, Lillie called the undertaker and made arrangements for another funeral. Suddenly, she realized she wasn't doing this just for Edward. She had lost a dear friend and sister in the Lord. With many conflicting feelings, she paid her last respects to Ada.

Now that Ada was gone, Lillie felt lonelier than ever. At sixty-three years of age, she had reached the season of life when most people think of retiring. But Lillie's history of working hard stayed with her. She hung a flyer advertising for work as a nanny. She waited breathlessly, unsure if anyone would answer her request or not. But one day not long after she had posted the flyer, she received a call.

"Hello, is this Lillie?" the voice asked.

"Yes." Lillie's hand shook as she held the receiver.

"My name is Dr. Showster. I am looking for a nanny for my children."

Lillie thought fast. *That sounds like a Jewish name. Some Jews are prejudiced against blacks.* "Excuse me, sir, but are you by any chance a Jew?" she asked.

Dr. Showster chuckled. "How did you know?"

"Your name gives me a big hint," Lillie said. "Before you hire me, I want you to know I'm black and also am a Christian. I pray and I witness wherever I am."

"As for your color, that doesn't make any difference to me, but I don't want you to be praying with my children," he said.

"I can't promise that, Doctor."

"I've heard good things about you, so I will hire you anyway," he said. "I'd like you to move to my house. How soon can you come?"

"Oh, I can come any time you want," Lillie said. "I'll just shut my old house up for a while. It's lonely now that I'm all alone."

Lillie moved to the doctor's beautiful home in the country. She loved six-year-old Jessica and nine-year-old Richard immediately. "You can call me Miz Lillie," she told them as soon as she settled into her bedroom suite upstairs. "How would you like to learn to play some games I played when I was a chile?"

Jessica giggled. "You were little once?"

Lillie smiled and tickled the little girl in the ribs. "Yes, I was. Do you know how to play hopscotch?"

Jessica shook her head. "No."

Lillie took her hand and led her out to the dirt beside the barn. Taking a sharp stick, she drew hopscotch squares. "All right, now you need to hop on one foot like this." Lillie hopped all the way to the end of the squares. "Ugh!" she said when she finished. "I must be gettin' old. That 'bout did me in."

Jessica clapped her hands. "Miz Lillie, I can do that." She held up her foot and nimbly hopped to the end of the marked squares.

"Good job," Lillie praised. "You are a natural. Now if you want it harder, you block one square and hop 'round it."

Jessica hopped and hopped. She taught her brother how to do it and they spent hours entertaining themselves.

One morning after Lillie had eaten breakfast with the children in the kitchen, Jessica spoke. "Miz Lillie? Why is your face always dirty?"

"Dirty?" Lillie laughed. "I ain't dirty, chile. Here, try to rub it off." She took the girl's finger and traced her own cheek. "See?"

"Oh, it stayed on," Jessica said innocently.

"Sure it does." Lillie was laughing so hard she was soon wiping tears. "That's how the good Lawd made me."

On Sundays, Lillie dressed the two children in their best and took them to Sunday school. "Miz Lillie," Richard said on the way home, "do you really think those Bible stories are true?"

"Indeedy!" Lillie said. "Every last one."

Richard frowned. "My daddy says I shouldn't believe everything you say."

Lillie smiled. "Don't jes' listen to only my words. I very well might make some mistakes. But Jesus always is true. You can believe all the time what He says."

Mrs. Showster expected Lillie to do much of the cooking, laundry, and cleaning. At age sixty-three, Lillie found the work tiring. Every morning, when she came down from her room, Mrs. Showster had a long list of chores for her to do. Lillie always did her best, but sometimes she felt she couldn't please the missus.

Lillie enjoyed laundry days most of all. She ran each batch through a modern washing machine, then hung them on the line. The sun shone, and the smell of flapping laundry transported her back to her childhood. Later she went out and took each piece off the line and tenderly pressed and folded them. She carried them to Mrs. Showster. "Here you are," Lillie said. "Everything dried quickly today."

Mrs. Showster sniffed. "Hope you did a good job and didn't cut any corners."

"As the good Lawd gives me strength, I do the best I can."

The next morning, Mrs. Showster met her at the door of the kitchen. "One of my favorite skirts is missing," she frowned.

"It is?" Lillie said, bewildered. She remembered laundering it with all the rest of the pieces and knew she had ironed and hung it with everything else.

"You took it, didn't you?" Mrs. Showster accused. "You were jealous and kept it for yourself. You won't get any pay this week to cover the loss."

Lillie's mouth dropped open. She felt again like she was living in the South, listening to her plantation owner. She clamped her mouth shut so she wouldn't say anything she would regret. She would search that house from top to bottom until she found that skirt.

She walked outside to the clothesline where she had hung the clothes. She checked the washing machine and the laundry basket. The skirt wasn't to be found. Lillie's heart sank. How could she convince Mrs. Showster she had never stolen anything from her?

That evening Lillie slowly climbed the stairs to her room. She knelt on the rag rug beside her bed. "Dear Lawd," she prayed, folding her hands and resting her forehead on them. "I'm in a deep quandary. I ask you to make that skirt appear somewhere."

The next morning, Lillie met Mrs. Showster at the bottom of the stairs. The lost skirt hung over her arm. "I owe you an apology, Miz Lillie," she said. "I found this skirt in the bottom of my closet this morning. I don't have any idea how it might have slipped off the hanger. Could you wash it and press it again for me?"

"Of course," Lillie said, smiling. "I knew the good Lawd would answer my prayer." She clapped her hands together and took the skirt.

Mrs. Showster also handed her the wages from last week. "I want to pay you for your hard work. You do a good job. I won't ever doubt your word again."

Lillie turned the iron on to heat once again. While she waited, she read her Bible at the kitchen table. Suddenly, Jessica burst through the door. "Miz Lillie, what are you reading?"

"It's my beloved Bible, chile. Now run along and play with your brother. I need to iron this skirt for your mama."

Jessica's eyes got big. "Did you bring the skirt back from where you stole it?"

Lillie chuckled. "The Lawd find it for His chile. Hallelujah!"

Lillie hurried to the ironing board and checked to see if the iron was hot. Carefully she smoothed the wrinkles from the skirt. She folded it neatly over the hanger and hung it in Mrs. Showster's closet before heading up to her room.

Lillie smiled as she carried her wages upstairs. "Lawd," she prayed, "you are so good to your chile."

chapter twenty-nine

Candy for Island Children

As Lillie and the Showster family walked down the wide hallways of the Pittsburgh International Airport, Lillie's heart beat fast. Today she would fly for the first time! Every year Dr. Showster took his family to the Balkan Islands, where he volunteered his medical skills to help poor islanders who lived in these impoverished Mediterranean countries.

"It's time to board," Lillie said as they approached their gate. "Follow us, Richard." Lillie took Jessica's hand to walk down the jetway.

"Can we swim every day?" Richard asked their nanny.

"I'm sure you can," Lillie said. "We will be at a resort, so there will be a lotta things for you to do."

Lillie hung on tightly to her armrests as the plane rattled and rumbled down the runway and soared into the air.

"Looky," Jessica said from the window seat, "the cars are getting small on the roads down there."

Lillie managed a quick look out the window. She felt her heart in her throat when she saw the ground below. She promptly pressed her head back against the headrest and closed her eyes. Only as the plane leveled out for a smooth ride to the Islands did she start to relax.

Some hours later, the plane descended toward the runway. "Look," Jessica said excitedly. "Are we going to land in the water?"

Lillie glanced out the window, then turned quickly to look out the windows across the aisle. All she could see was water. "I hope not." Lillie tried to console Jessica, but she secretly hoped the pilot knew what he was doing. Pretty soon Lillie felt a small bump and the plane slid to a stop on the short runway. Lillie sighed with relief and flexed her fingers, stiff from clenching the armrests. Flying definitely wasn't her favorite thing to do! The plane taxied to the terminal. After deplaning, Lillie and the Showster family collected their luggage from the baggage carousel inside the airport.

Dr. Showster hailed a taxi. "Good morning," the driver said, doffing his hat. "Welcome to our island."

One by one the family climbed into the vehicle while the driver loaded their luggage in the trunk. Lillie stood near the trunk, watching to make sure that none of the suitcases stayed behind.

"Are you the nanny?" the driver asked Lillie.

"Yes, I am," she said.

"Don't let your little charges outside the resort. There are poor people who will take advantage of rich children like these."

Lillie nodded. She understood what he said, but at the same time she wished she could slip away and help these poor people.

Dr. Showster settled his family and Lillie in a luxurious hotel. Palm trees waved in the tropical breeze.

"I wish I could stay with you," Dr. Showster said. "But I need to be closer to the local people so I can doctor them." His mind had already shifted from his family into physician mode. Lillie saw the passion in his eyes as he packed medicines into a suitcase and headed out to a nearby village with the taxi driver. Lillie knew he would do his best to give them all the medical help he could.

Lillie stayed with Mrs. Showster and the children at the hotel. Following Mrs. Showster's lead, Lillie unpacked the children's belongings and her own in the elaborate bedrooms. *Mmm, mmm, mmm,* she thought, running her hand over the glossy finish of a stately mahogany dresser. *Jes' look at all these fine things.* She chuckled gleefully when she wondered what Pappaw and Mammaw would have thought if they could have seen their little Lillie in a place like this. *All the way from a slave cabin to a rich white man's resort in the Mediterranean!* Then she sobered. *I guess this is what I always said I wanted—to live like rich folks.* She looked around at the elegant tapestries, the plush bedding covering deep, soft mattresses, the carpet so thick she thought a body surely could sleep on it. *Wonder why they can't be happy, with all this. I know Pappaw always said, "It's people who make us rich."* Lillie knew she was too drawn to fancy things. *Guess I surely ought to get my fill on this trip!*

After a good night's sleep, they went downstairs for breakfast. Lillie's mouth dropped open at the smorgasbord of boiled eggs, pancakes, fruit, sausage, bacon, waffles, juice, coffee, and every kind of breakfast food they could want. Her wide eyes took in the array of unfamiliar dishes on another table, and she went to have a closer look. She nodded approvingly at the hard breads, soft cheeses, and olives so salty they puckered her mouth and made her eyes water. Lots of fish, both pickled and raw, swam in olive oil. She sniffed doubtfully at a bowl of something that looked suspiciously like curdled milk. *Whooee!* She jerked back, eyebrows climbing. *Can't imagine scoopin' that up first thing in the mornin'!* Stepping back, Lillie decided to watch and see if any of the local people took any of the strange foods before she tried them.

Lillie helped the children get their food, then took them to the veranda and settled them at a table overlooking the sea. Lillie thought she could watch the sea all day. She nibbled the delicacies slowly, trying to make them last as long as possible. What were they going to do for the rest of the day once they were done eating? She didn't have to wait long to find out.

The children gobbled their food and hopped to their feet. "Let's go swimming," Richard yelled. They ran across the veranda and up the stairs. In just a few minutes, they returned in their swimwear with towels draped over their arms. Throwing his towel haphazardly over a chair, Richard ran to the pool, took a big leap, and landed with a wild splash in the pool.

His sister Jessica daintily dipped her toes in the water and sat on the edge of the pool, watching Richard. "Come on, Sis!" Richard called.

"I'll watch you from here."

"Aw, come on!"

Lillie walked across the terrace and sat beside the little girl. "Shall I teach you to swim?" she asked. "Then you can be a fish like Richard."

"Would you?" Jessica asked eagerly.

"Of course. I'll run get my bathin' suit, and I'll be right back."

Soon Lillie was back with her full body swimsuit with stockings. She plunged in and swam laps around the pool. As she neared the little girl sitting on the edge, she stopped in front of her, treading water to keep afloat. "Where did you learn to swim?" Jessica's eyes shone.

"When I was a teenager, my town offered swimming lessons to blacks like myself. I spent many hours after school swimmin' laps at the Y. Come," she said, holding out her arms. "I'll hold you and show you how to float."

Jessica hesitated and then slowly reached out to grab Lillie's shoulders as she slipped into the water. "Now, let go of me," Lillie said. "Don't be afraid. I'll hold you up."

Jessica's grip slowly relaxed, and Lillie held her as she showed her how to float. "Good girl," Lillie encouraged. "Now, kick your feet and paddle with your arms."

One morning as Lillie lazily watched the ocean from her deck chair, Jessica called from the pool. "Watch me, Miz Lillie. I can swim!" Lillie watched with pleasure as Jessica doggy-paddled around the pool.

"Very good, Jessica. You're learnin' fast," she said. Lillie yawned. She had already had her fill of doing nothing. She wanted to get out and see how the island people really lived.

The next morning after brunch, Lillie stopped beside the deck chair where the doctor's wife was lounging. "Mrs. Showster, would you watch the children today? I would like to see firsthand what the doctor is doin' for the people."

Mrs. Showster's brows lifted. "I can't imagine why you would want to see filthy, diseased people." She waved her arm, dismissing Lillie. "Go ahead. I'll watch the children today."

Without a moment's hesitation, Lillie hurried out to the nearest store and filled a bag with candy. She chose to walk down the road instead of calling a taxi. As soon as she left the resort, the roads were filled with huge potholes. Sewage ran down the sides of the street. Her stomach repulsed at the filth, but when she saw all the children, she felt such compassion that she forgot about the horrible conditions around her.

"Come here, little one," she said holding out her hand to a skinny little boy. He looked like a scared rabbit ready to bound away. "Do you like candy?"

The boy walked closer and inspected what she held in her hand. He put out his hand and touched it.

"You can have it." She nodded, knowing he didn't understand a word she said.

He grabbed it and ran for a tumbledown shack nearby. Lillie could see it wasn't fit for human habitation. How she longed for these village people to feel the love of God!

As she stood there wondering what she should do next, a swarm of children surrounded her and motioned to their mouths. Lillie laughed. "You all want candy?" she asked, motioning so they would understand.

They jabbered excitedly.

Soon all her candy had disappeared. Now what should she do? How she wished she could do more to minister to their physical needs. She slowly wandered back toward the resort. As she meandered down one street, a street vendor called out. "Missu, missu, missu, buya from me."

She stopped in front of the man's stand and fingered the tasseled scarves, the beaded leather hearts, and the locally made pottery. What could she buy to help these people in their poverty?

The vendor pressed in close. "Five dolla'," he said, pointing to a painted bowl. "Five dolla'?"

Lillie shook her head. She knew his price was too high.

"Three dolla'," he insisted. "Just three dolla'."

Lillie hesitated. "Two?" she asked, holding up two fingers.

The man nodded. Wrapping the bowl carefully in paper, he handed it to her, and Lillie placed the money in his hand. "Thank you," he said, bowing slightly.

She waved as she turned to walk down the street. Her purchase seemed like a small thing, but she hoped she had helped some poor man buy food for his family.

The month passed quickly, and one afternoon Dr. Showster returned to the resort. After Lillie had tucked her charges in bed that night, she relaxed in the lounge with the doctor and his wife. "The needs are so great, and I can do so little," Dr. Showster lamented. He reached for his wine bottle on the coffee table and poured the red liquid into a glass. He took a sip, then another, and soon had drained it.

"But you are doin' somethin'," Lillie encouraged.

"But there's always more to do. What more can be done?" Dr. Showster poured himself another glass of wine. Lillie felt sad that he turned to drink to make him forget the horrible things he saw.

Mrs. Showster said nothing as she sipped her wine in silence.

"Dr. Showster," Lillie said. "Ministerin' to these people's physical needs is a great service, but what they really need is to be ministered to spiritually."

Dr. Showster waved his hand in dismissal. "You know I don't agree."

"Maybe not," Lillie said stoutly, "but I've witnessed so many lives changed in my life that I went out one day with a bag of candy, intendin' to find a way to show these people the love of my Lawd Jesus."

"I'm sure you didn't get very far without an interpreter." Dr. Showster's mouth twisted cynically.

Mrs. Showster yawned. "I don't know why you would waste your time on these people. I'm going to bed." She turned, and Lillie watched as she disappeared down the hall.

Lillie stood up to leave too. "At least I showed 'em a little of the love of God," she said. "And I pray someday you will experience the same." Lillie turned and glanced at the doctor before going into her room. He said nothing, but his unsteady hand gripped the goblet tighter as he gazed out the window into the darkness. Her heart ached with sadness, knowing the doctor might never experience healing in his own heart like the healing his capable hands brought to others.

Lillie felt glad to be on the ground again after their flight home. "Thank you for going with us to the Balkans," Dr. Showster said briskly. "I'm sorry to tell you this, but because of your strange beliefs, I think it would be better if you would pack your bags and leave our house."

Lillie's insides curdled. But she nodded submissively. "Well, I can do that. My Lawd will never let me down. If you don't want me, I'll find another nanny job."

Dr. Showster shuffled uncomfortably. "It's not that you haven't done a good job, but you just make me nervous with all your ideas. We have decided to look for another nanny."

"As you wish, Dr. Showster. I've enjoyed workin' for you. Your children will always be in my heart."

The next morning, Lillie packed her bags, praying all the time. When she came downstairs, Dr. and Mrs. Showster were nowhere around. She propped her satchel by the front door and took Jessica in her arms. Richard stood awkwardly beside her. She touched his arm. "I'll miss you both," Lillie choked.

Jessica swiped at her eyes. "Me too, Miz Lillie."

"Always remember the Jesus I taught you." Lillie kissed them both, picked up her bags, and headed out the door without a second glance. She didn't want the children to see the pain she felt in parting with them.

It's good to be home, Lillie thought as she walked up her front steps. Opening the door to the silent house, she noticed the dust that had collected during her stint at Dr. Showster's. She sniffed at the stale air and opened a few windows to let in the fresh breeze. In spite of the empty feeling, it felt good to be home. Dusting off her trusty old chair, she sighed as she sank into it and closed her eyes. Her bones ached almost as much as her heart. "Lawd, I think I'm not meant to live on this earth. My husband is gone, my friends are gone, I just lost my job, and . . . and I feel disconnected from my church." She suddenly felt guilty that she hadn't been to church. "I've been living with Dr. Showster's family so long and had little opportunity to go to church. Lawd, guide my next step." She rocked for a long time, allowing her body and spirit to adjust to the silent spaces of her old home. Her heart yearned to settle into a church home as well. But twenty long years would pass before God met that need.

chapter thirty

"These Unusual People"

"My husband is dead and gone," Agatha Thompson spat out one day, "and a good thing he is, too."

Lillie frowned, wondering if the dignified old woman had lost her mind. She laid down her dust rag and turned to face the woman she served as caretaker. "But, Agatha, your husband was a good old man."

"Huh?!" Agatha harrumphed. "He pulled the wool over everyone's eyes." Agatha got face to face with her Lillie. "He was an evil man," she whispered confidentially. "He molested every one of our children."

Lillie blinked in surprise. She reached out her wrinkled hand and took the other woman's gnarled hand in hers. "Only God can help you to forgive your husband."

Agatha pulled her hand back and shook her head as her bitter words poured forth. She would not forgive.

Lillie's heart went out to the old woman. She had faced her own battles with bitterness toward her husband, Ed. As she resumed dusting the furniture, she thanked the Lord for the miracle of His grace at work in her heart. Over and over again she had chosen to forgive, and the Lord had given her grace to love and serve those who wronged her.

Loving and giving to others had become a way of life for Lillie. As she poured out her life in providing companion care for many elderly people throughout her seventies and eighties, Lillie didn't seem to realize she was aging herself. "I'm not the old one," she convinced herself, "they're the ones who need the help."

But Lillie also needed a place where she could be nourished spiritually. Hungry for fellowship, Lillie turned from one church to another. Her search led her through numerous churches, but each time, things turned sour. A pastor who fell into adultery; teaching that tilted heavily toward law, with little grace; and unrelenting demands to give more money to the church. *Where can I find a church that is true to God and His Word?* Lillie wondered. Still, she refused to give up or yield to disillusionment.

One spring morning in 2008, Lillie sat on her front porch, her Bible draped on her lap. Folding her careworn, wrinkled hands, she turned her eyes heavenward. "Lawd," she prayed, "my life is in your hands. As you lead me, I want to follow. I don't feel too kindly right now toward many of the churches I have visited. I pray now for a touch from your hand." Painfully, Lillie groped for her cane. Leaning heavily on it, she went back into her kitchen for her car keys and wallet. Stopping to take a breath, she continued her prayer. "Lawd, I need a place to belong as I finish my earthly course."

She walked over to her old Lincoln Continental and ran a hand gently over its hood. This worn-out car had been her constant companion through the years, always a reminder of Ed's sin and God's redemption. "I miss you, Ed," she whispered. She drove the short distance to Valesky's Grocery in Clearmill.

Putting her cane in the cart, she leaned on her cart as she pushed it up and down the aisles. Flour, sugar, eggs, milk, cheese. One by one she crossed items off her list. As she rounded a corner, she noticed a uniquely-dressed woman down the cereal aisle. The woman wore a long dress, much the same as the ladies from the Apostolic Church Lillie had left years ago. The woman's hair was neatly combed back under a cloth veil. Her face held a peaceful look. Desire and curiosity gripped Lillie. She had to know who this woman was. She wheeled her cart over to her. "Hello, ma'am," she said. "It's my pleasure to meet you."

The woman looked up from her shopping. "Hello, my name is Betty," she said pleasantly.

"I'm Sister Lillie."

"Glad to meet you, Sister Lillie." Betty set a box of cereal in her cart. "What can I do for you?"

"I don't want to be rude, but I can't help myself. Can I ask where you go to church?"

Betty smiled. "I'm not offended. We go to Living Waters Fellowship."

"Do you allow strangers to visit?"

"Of course. Would you like to come?"

Lillie smiled. "I surely would. Can you tell me where to find you?"

Betty gave Lillie the address, and Lillie stuffed the paper into her ample purse. She would check them out on Sunday. She missed her church family so much, yet she no longer felt comfortable there. She knew she needed to find another church. She checked out quickly and headed home.

"I wonder what that church is like," she murmured to herself. She carefully put away her groceries before making herself a pot of soup with her fresh vegetables.

The next Sunday, Lillie woke with a start. "I promised Betty I would come to her church this mornin'." She dressed as quickly as her eighty-three-year-old bones would allow, and hurried to the kitchen. Taking her purse, Lillie unzipped it and rooted around until she found the paper with the address on it. Lillie grabbed her cane and hobbled out the door. The Mennonite church was farther away than she thought, but she still arrived early.

"Hello," a gray-haired man said as she entered the small church house. "I'm Nathan Martin."

"You the pastor here?" Lillie asked.

"Yes, I am, and what's your name?"

"Lillie Clark. Pastor Nathan, I love the Lawd. Do you throw out old negroes like myself, or can I visit your church?"

"Jesus never threw out anyone. We don't either. You are most welcome," he said, motioning toward the sanctuary. "Please find a seat."

Lillie leaned on her cane as she walked all the way to the front of the room. A woman smiled at her and motioned for her to sit next to her. "Welcome," she said. "My name is Teresa."

"I'm Sister Lillie," Lillie said, sitting down heavily beside her. She looked across the sanctuary and saw the families sitting together, looking happy in the Lord. She immediately remembered her prayer for a church family so many years ago when she had left the Showster family. Was this the hand of God? She closed her eyes and raised her hands to heaven. "Jesus, thank you for these unusual people! Have you brought me here to finish my course?" A few people looked around discreetly to see who was speaking aloud, but Lillie didn't notice.

As the service started and the congregation joined their voices in song, Lillie thought she had never heard anything more beautiful. She swayed in her seat and clapped her hands. "Amen!" she cried.

When Pastor Nathan rose to preach, Lillie thought she was seeing the face of Jesus. "Good morning," he welcomed the congregation. "And a special welcome to Sister Lillie."

Lillie nodded. "Praise the Lawd!" she said loudly, barely able to contain herself.

The service introduced new concepts to Lillie. For the first time, she heard about brotherhood, accountability, and discipleship. "I've never heard anything like it," she said to Nathan and Teresa as she sat at their kitchen table after church that day. "When you were up there preachin' the Gospel I saw the face of Jesus. Oh, yes, I did."

Nathan chuckled.

"And I don't think no church people has ever asked me for dinner. You are too kind." Lillie filled her plate and started eating. "Tell me who you Mennonites are anyway."

"Have you never heard of the Anabaptist faith in history?" Nathan asked. Lillie shook her head. "Never."

Nathan rose and walked to his office. Soon he returned with a couple books. "I love history. Do you enjoy reading?"

"Yes, I do," Lillie said.

"Take these books home, and you can read about their experiences. They were rebaptized as believers and rejected by the Catholic Church. Many were killed for what the church said was a heretical faith."

When Lillie got home, she sat right down and started reading. Twelve men in a dungeon who refused to recant. Michael Sattler's tongue being cut out before he was burned at the stake. This was a faith that was strong and unrelenting. Even a thirteen-year-old girl burned because of her faith. "Praise the Lawd!" Lillie cried. "This Mennonite faith lives the Word of God!"

Lillie kept going to this new strange church. Ladies sent her hot meals, granola, and flowers. They showed her such love that she couldn't deny God in their lives. Yet she couldn't quite understand their culture any more than they could understand hers. "We'll just keep a-workin' on it," Lillie declared to Teresa and Nathan, her new Mennonite friends. "As long as we love the Lawd, we can figure it out some way!"

chapter thirty-one

Katherine

L illie reached for her phone. She had been attending the Mennonite church regularly for three years now, and it had been a while since she had invited Katherine to go along to church with her. "I'm gonna try again. Surely she'll go with me one of these times." The phone rang and rang and rang. "That's strange," Lillie thought. "She always answers when I call. Maybe she's gone. I'll try again tomorrow."

Lillie called the next day and the next. Each time she called there was no answer. Something wasn't right. Lillie finally called her son. "Eddie, do you know if Katherine is gone somewhere?"

"Not that I know of. Seems you would know if she had."

Lillie agreed. "I don't remember her tellin' me anything about leavin'. But I've tried now three days, and she hasn't answered her phone. I'm afraid somethin' is wrong. Would you mind going past her house and checkin' on her?"

"Sure, Mama Lillie, I'll go right away," Edward Jr. said.

The phone rang again. "Mama!" Edward Jr. cried. "I'm here with

Katherine. I'm loadin' her up and takin' her to the hospital. Can you come right away?"

"What happened, Eddie?"

"I'll talk about it when you get to the hospital. Hurry, Mama!"

Driving had become more difficult for Lillie as she aged, so she called her old friend Thelma, who drove her to the hospital as fast as she could. Lillie hurried into the hospital and to the front desk. "Please tell me where my daughter is!" she gasped.

"Just a minute, ma'am, we'll need to get some information from you," the secretary replied calmly. "What's your daughter's name?" Lillie calmed down enough to answer the questions and finally got the information she needed.

"Your daughter's in Intensive Care, Room 212. I'll call them so they know you are coming."

Thelma helped Lillie onto the elevator, and they got off at the second floor. Lillie's cane tapped a quick staccato down the halls until she came to two locked double doors. She pounded on them. "Look here." Thelma pointed to the wall. "Just pick up this receiver, and it will get you to the desk inside."

Lillie picked up the phone. "I want to see my daughter in Room 212."

The double doors unlocked as if by magic and swung open. Lillie held Thelma's arm as they hurried down the hall to Katherine's room. The door was shut, but when Lillie knocked softly, Edward Jr. came out, shutting the door behind him. Tears ran down his cheeks.

Lillie grabbed his arm, the wrinkles on her dark face accented by the worry in her heart. "Eddie, tell me she is all right!"

Edward Jr. put his arms around her. "Mama, when I got to her house, I knocked and knocked. I could see lights on, but no one came to the door. I finally picked the lock and broke in. Katherine was lying on the floor. It looked like she had been there a long time. She was unable to move. Oh, Mama, I was so devastated. I talked to her, but she didn't seem to be able to answer me. I saw she was still breathin', so I called the ambulance. I sat and rubbed her cold arms and legs until they arrived. I wished you had been there, Mama. I didn't know what to say to her or how to pray. When the paramedics got there, they confirmed that she had had a stroke. And I just want to warn you, Mama, they have her all hooked up to machines. She is completely on life support."

Lillie broke down in sobs and then wiped her eyes. "I want to see her," she said, squaring her shoulders. She turned to Thelma. "Thank you for bringing me."

"Did you want me to stay?" Thelma asked.

Lillie wanted to be alone with her children. "No, you can go on home. I'll be all right now that Edward Jr. is with me."

"Call me if you need anything." Thelma gave Lillie a quick hug before she left.

Edward Jr. led her into the room. Lillie looked at the still form on the bed. "Katherine?" she called. "Can you hear me?"

Katherine didn't move. No twitch of the eyelid, no toes wiggling, nothing. Her whole left side hung motionless. Lillie stepped bravely to the bed and laid her hand on her daughter, just as Pappaw had laid his hand on her so many years ago. She prayed simply, believing. "In the name of Jesus, I ask you to heal my daughter."

"Eddie," Lillie turned to her son, "I'm stayin' right by her side. Could you please go tell Pastor Nathan to come? I need the Spirit of the Lawd here with me."

"Who's he?" Edward Jr. looked at his mother strangely.

"He's the pastor at the church I've been attending. One who has love for the brothers and sisters. This pastor preaches the whole Word of God. I believe God sent me there to finish my days on this earth."

"Whatever you say, Mama," Edward Jr. said wearily. "How can I contact this pastor?"

"I have his number beside my phone at home. Please call him and tell him Sister Lillie asked if he would come to the hospital. And, Eddie, could you please call Maria and William? I know Katherine hasn't had much contact with her children lately, but I think they should know."

Edward Jr. left, and Lillie sat next to her daughter. She massaged Katherine's limp left arm. Her daughter didn't respond. About an hour later Lillie heard a knock on the hospital door. "Can we come in?"

"Yes," Lillie called.

Pastor Nathan and his wife walked in and stood by the bed. "Your son called us, and we came right over."

"Oh, Pastor," cried Lillie, heartbroken. "Something's wrong with my Katherine. She's young and healthy. Now she's had a stroke and seems paralyzed on her left side."

"May we pray with you?"

Together they bowed their heads, laying hands on the silent form on the bed. Pastor Nathan led in prayer. "God, you are our Father, and we know you are looking down on this hospital bed right now. We pray for you to heal Katherine in the name of Jesus. Most of all, I ask that you will give Lillie peace in her heart and wisdom as she sits with her daughter day after day. In your blessed name, Amen!"

"Amen! Hallelujah!" Lillie cried.

"Call us if you need anything else," Teresa said.

"I will, and from the bottom of my ol' heart I thank you for coming."

Nathan smiled. "We will stop in again tomorrow to see how she's doing. We will be in prayer for you and your daughter."

"Thank you," Lillie said. "I 'preciate that."

She watched, bracing herself with a gnarled hand on the doorjamb, as they left her, walking down the hall holding hands. "How I wish me and my Edward coulda had a love like that." She bowed her head and thanked God again for leading her to these people.

Every day, Lillie came and sat by Katherine's side and prayed. One day, while Lillie rubbed Katherine's arm, it jerked. "Oh, thank you, Lawd, she's comin' 'round." Lillie wiped the saliva seeping out of her daughter's mouth. Just then, Katherine reached over and touched Lillie's hand. "Katherine, can you hear me?"

Katherine opened her eyes for a moment before closing them again.

The next day, when Lillie got to the hospital, the nurse told her that Katherine had improved enough to be moved out of the Intensive Care unit. Hurrying to Katherine's new room, Lillie found Katherine lying on her bed with her eyes open. "Katherine, it's your mama," she cried.

Lillie's heart swelled with joy when Katherine smiled and nodded slightly.

All day, she continued to improve. Within the week, she tried to talk. "M–m–Mama," she said. "Wh–wh–why am I o–on th–this b–b–bed?" Her struggling speech sounded like music to Lillie's ears.

"You were sick, my girl. But now I see the Lawd is healin' you, and you're gonna make it."

Three days later, Katherine walked a few steps with a walker. "Come on," Lillie encouraged. "You can do it."

"She's a wonder," the doctor said. "I've never seen such quick recovery."

Lillie chuckled. "She is that and more."

Every day, there were visitors from church to cheer Lillie. "You people have been so nice to me," Lillie told Nathan on one of their visits. "I thank God for your support."

Katherine made quick progress, and the doctor soon released her. "You need to come home with me," Lillie insisted.

Katherine didn't argue. Edward Jr. came and took them to Lillie's house. Lillie called her grandchildren again. "You need to come see your mama," she told them. "She almost died, you know."

Katherine's children never came. They called from their far-off homes in Ohio, but never felt it necessary to travel to see their mother.

Lillie went with her daughter to her follow up appointment to see what caused her stroke. "You have a brain tumor," the doctor bluntly told Katherine.

"A what?" Lillie exclaimed, startled. She glanced at her daughter to see a tear trickling down her cheek.

The doctor looked at Katherine. Gently, he said, "I'm sorry to give you all this bad news. I will refer you to a surgeon. You need to see him right away."

"Oh, doctor, are you sure?" Lillie cried out.

"Yes," the doctor said. "The sooner she goes, the more chance of getting it before it grows too big to get it out."

As they left the doctor's office, Katherine said nothing.

They drove home in silence. When they got to the driveway, Lillie broached the subject. "God is with us, Katherine, and He won't leave us now. I think you should make an appointment with the surgeon right away." Lillie said no more as she helped Katherine settle into her bedroom.

Worry and tension hung in the air, but Katherine refused to talk about the tumor. Lillie wondered if the inability to pay for this surgery and the daunting diagnosis were too much for Katherine to cope with. She tried not to pry any more into her daughter's business, but instead took it to her heavenly Father in prayer. "I'm available for you in any way I can help," she told her daughter.

A few days later, Katherine said suddenly, "I have my surgery scheduled for next week. They told me it is an eight-hour surgery."

Lillie reached for her daughter and put her arms around her. Katherine didn't pull away.

The day for the surgery arrived. Edward Jr. and Lillie took Katherine to the hospital. Not sure how they would pass the time, they decided to sit in the waiting room. One hour passed. Then two. Then three. Lillie worried that something was wrong. "Eddie, why aren't they telling us anything?" she asked.

"Don't worry, Mama," he reassured her. "They will tell us somethin' when they have somethin' to tell. Until then we just wait."

Four hours after they started, a nurse came out. "Are you here with Katherine?" she asked.

"Yes, Nurse, what can you tell us?" Lillie asked.

"She's doing well. They have the biggest tumor out, but there are two smaller ones yet to be removed. We are taking good care of her."

Eight hours later, the surgery was finished. The doctor told them they could see Katherine for a moment, but she wouldn't be coherent until morning. Edward Jr. walked with Lillie back to her room and waited while Lillie walked over to the bed. She rubbed Katherine's arm, smoothed back her hair, and told her they would be back.

The next morning, Lillie hurried to the hospital eager to see her daughter. The nurse at the desk stopped her. "Mrs. Clark?"

"Yes?"

"The doctor would like to see you before you see your daughter. Could you wait in the family room until he can see you?"

"What's wrong?" Lillie demanded. "Did the surgery not go as well as they thought?"

The nurse picked up her phone. "Doctor, Lillie Clark is here." She hung up the phone and looked over the desk at Lillie. "He will see you soon."

Lillie shook as she sat down in a chair in the family waiting room. "Lawd, you been healin' her up to this point, are you gonna stop now?"

The door opened and the white-clad doctor came in. "Hello, I'm Doctor Wilson. I wanted to prepare you for the condition your daughter is in."

"Is she still livin'?" Lillie asked, hands clenched together in her lap.

The doctor nodded. "The tumors were deep and embedded. The surgery was much more involved than we ever imagined. She was a trooper through it all. But surgery brought swelling to her brain, and we actually put her on a ventilator until her body starts functioning again. She's still a very sick woman."

Lillie nodded. She swiped a tear from her cheek. "She's a fighter. She'll pull through it if anyone does."

Katherine lay unmoving for three weeks. Lillie sang and prayed and begged God to spare her daughter's life. One day as Lillie sat reading her Bible and praying, Lillie noticed movement from the bed. "Oh, Lawd, she's wigglin' her toes." Lillie hurried to Katherine's side. "Katherine, can you hear me?" The toes wiggled again.

Edward Jr. came to the hospital that evening to visit. "Mama Lillie, you need a break. I'll take you to church Sunday if you like."

Lillie's tired eyes came alive. "You will? Really, Eddie?"

Edward Jr. nodded. "I will. But don't expect me singin' and rejoicin' like you do."

Lillie clapped her hands. "Praise de Lawd, you're answerin' all my prayers! Now my son is goin' with me to church. Woo-hoo!" Her loud voice made heads turn to see the cause of the commotion.

Edward Jr. touched his mama's arm. "Mama Lillie, calm down. You need to come with me. You go home and get a good night's sleep and go to church tomorrow, then I'll bring you back here."

Lillie gathered her things together, and hanging onto her son's arm for support, walked with him to his car. "Thanks, Eddie, I needed some time away."

When Edward Jr. dropped her off that evening, he promised to be there first thing in the morning. Lillie couldn't sleep that night. She spent hours in prayer for her son at his home and her daughter lying in the hospital.

chapter thirty-two

Treasure in Heaven

The next morning, Edward Jr. pulled in and parked in front of Lillie's apartment. Opening his car door, he hoisted himself out of the driver's seat and hurried to the front door. Lillie met him, fiddling with something on her head. "Mama?" Edward Jr. stared at her head. "Whatsa that black thing on the back of your head?"

"Don't ya worry yourself about it, Eddie. God sent me to finish my course with my Mennonite friends. They have taught me that to honor the God I love, I will cover my head. For Him, Eddie, for my precious Lawd."

Edward Jr. sighed. "Mama, sometimes I think you are losing your mind."

"Not me," Lillie chuckled as she climbed slowly into the passenger side of the car. Edward Jr. shook his head as he shut her door and hurried around to the driver's side, put the car in gear, and began to drive to Living Waters Fellowship.

Edward Jr. parked close to the church entrance. Then he helped Lillie out and held her arm as she proudly led her son to the front bench. Edward Jr. dutifully sat beside her, hoping no one would notice him. Lillie watched him closely during the service. She could see that he wasn't allowing the Lord's Spirit to call him yet. "Nice church," he said on their way back to the hospital.

Lillie bit back the impatient words on the tip of her tongue. How she wished her son could experience the spiritual richness she had found in this church! She needed to trust God's Spirit to draw her son in His timing.

As Lillie walked into Katherine's room that afternoon, she knew she was experiencing a miracle from God firsthand. Katherine was sitting on a chair. "Mama," she said when Lillie walked in, "it's about time you came to see me."

"I've been here every day for the last three weeks," Lillie told her. "But all you could do was wiggle your toes."

Katherine blinked. "I woke up not long ago and sat up. I felt a little dizzy, so I lay back down. When the nurse came in, I asked if she could help me to a chair. She looked so surprised I wasn't sure if she would help me."

That afternoon, the doctor stopped in at Katherine's room on his daily rounds. "Looks like you're every bit the firecracker your mother said you were." His eyes twinkled.

Two days later, Katherine walked out of the hospital, healed. She had no trace of cancer in her body. "Hallelujah, Jesus!" Lillie said. She waved her hands in praise, but kept her voice down, remembering the stir she caused last time she let loose in the hospital halls.

Edward Jr. took his sister home with him. He counted out her medication every day and took total care of her. He made sure she could care for herself completely before she moved back into her own home. It did Lillie's heart good to see the love between them.

The crisis with Katherine had passed. But several years later, Lillie faced another medical crisis in her family. Early in 2014, she got a phone call about her brother, Walker. He had moved to a nearby town a few years before.

"Lillie, Walker's in the hospital. He need someone to come sit with him and help him." It was Walker's friend. Walker had never married and had no one to care for him.

"What's wrong with him?" Lillie's heart felt saddened to hear that her brother was ill.

"He sick with pneumonia, I think that's what they sayin'," the man said.

Once again, Lillie made regular trips to the hospital, plodding down the corridors with her cane tapping alongside her. The nurses got used to seeing her day after day at her brother's bedside.

One day, as Lillie sat by Walker's bedside, Edward Jr. called. "Mama Lillie, are you at home?"

Lillie sensed an urgency in his voice. "No, I'm with your Uncle Walker."

Edward Jr. sighed with relief. "I drove past your place, and your house was ablaze. I drove to a nearby phone booth and called the fire station. They are on their way."

"Oh, Lawd!" Lillie cried aloud. "What are you doing now? Haven't you chastened me enough?"

"Mama Lillie? Are you gonna be okay?"

Lillie felt herself shaking. "I dunno."

"Shall I come get you?"

"No. No, I should stay with Walker."

"You sure?"

"Yes," Lillie said, not sure at all as she grappled with the reality of the blow.

Lillie remembered that a Mennonite brother lived near her house. She dialed his number. "Brian," she said, "my house is all afire. I'm in the hospital with my brother. Could you go check it out and call me back? Surely it isn't as bad as Eddie thinks."

"Sure, I can," Brian said. "Do you have a number where I can reach you?"

Lillie gave him the number to reach her at the hospital. She sat waiting, and when the phone rang about ten minutes later she answered it immediately. "Brother Brian, is my house all right?"

Brian cleared his throat. "It looks bad. I can't get very close, Sister Lillie, because the police blocked the streets near the house. It is so cold the water is turning to icicles as it pours out of the hoses." January was the coldest month of the year in Clearmill.

"Can't you give me some hope? Am I gonna lose everything?"

Brian hesitated. "It doesn't look good at all. Do you need a ride? If you want to see for yourself, I can come and pick you up at the hospital and take you there."

"I think I'd better go see," Lillie said, changing her mind.

Lillie stood in front of the hospital entrance, gripping her cane, waiting for Brian to arrive. She climbed into the passenger seat, and he sped away. As they neared her street she saw lights flashing and smoke billowing. She got out of the car and stood in shock, watching the flames destroy her home. She lifted her hands to the sky, "The Lawd giveth, the Lawd taketh away, blessed be the name of the Lawd."

Only a shell remained of Lillie's home. Suddenly friends surrounded her. Each one asked what they could do and if she needed a place to stay.

When Lillie turned around, she saw Edward Jr. pulling up to the curb. He jumped out of his car, ran to his mother, and put his arm around her. "I figured you'd find a way here. Mama, come home with us. You have nothing here. I'm ready to help you all I can."

Numbly, Lillie followed him to his car. She sat in the back and leaned her head against the seat. "I can't believe it," she said aloud. "I lost everything—my will, old coins from Edward, my clothes, my books, my photos—everythin's gone. Destroyed." Her heart sank to the soles of her shoes. For the first time, she felt the weight of every one of her eighty-nine years. "What should I do?" she prayed.

The next morning, Edward Jr. sat beside his mother. "Now, Mama," he said, "I know you can't remember everything you lost, but I need to start replacing documents and things like that. Can you try to tell me what you can think of right now?"

Lillie sighed. "I'll try." She wrinkled her face in concentration. "My license, my will, my insurance, my banking CDs . . . oh, Eddie, how will we ever get everything replaced? All my nice things!" she mourned.

Edward Jr. picked up his phone and dialed first one place then another. Five hours later, he scooted his chair back from the table, having done all he could. "Now, Mama, we need to take you to the store. Among other things, you will need some new clothes."

"I don't have money for new clothes, Eddie."

"Don't worry. Your friends gave me some money last night and told me to take you to get what you needed."

"They did?" Lillie's jaw dropped. Memories of her earlier experience with money and the church flashed through her head. They weren't good memories. Maybe these people were different after all.

She shivered in her light dress. "I guess I do need a coat," she said, following her son out to his car.

At the store, Edward Jr. waited patiently while she found a coat to fit, some house dresses, and a few sundries. Lillie thought back to the days at Grapple when she washed her only dress every day. She could do that again until she could afford more.

Back in the car, she sat by her son as they drove back to his home. "Aren't you sad, Mama?" Edward Jr. asked.

Lillie sighed. "Clothes and my house furnishings can be replaced," she said, "but I can't replace the coins your dad collected, my documents, and all the photos of you and Katherine as young'uns."

Edward Jr. reached over and squeezed her hand. "I know, Mama."

Lillie wiped a tear from her eye. "But my Jesus, He tells me He's making me a mansion in the sky. Why should I care what I have on this ol' earth?"

After supper, Edward Jr. drove her over to see what was left of her house.

When she saw the collapsed roof, the crumbled walls, and the heaps of ashes, she knew it would have to be leveled and probably wouldn't be rebuilt. "What do I do now, Eddie? I can't live with you long term."

"Your friends told me they would start looking for a place for you to live," Edward Jr. said. "They have been doing all they can to lighten the burden for us. Those people are some of the best."

Lillie nodded, feeling overwhelmed by all the generosity. The next Sunday, she took the opportunity to thank her Mennonite friends for their support during her traumatic time.

Within a few weeks, Teresa called her. "Hello, Lillie?"

"Hello, my friend. Praise de Lawd!" Lillie answered.

"Nathan and I want to show you a place for rent that I think would be exactly what you are looking for." Excitement tinged Teresa's voice.

"Really? Today?" Lillie asked.

"Sure, we'll pick you up in a half hour."

"Okay, I'll be waitin'." Lillie got her coat and her cane and stood watching out the window until she saw them drive in. "Eddie," she called. "I'm going to look at a place for rent."

She climbed in the back of Nathan's car. Lillie watched the road they were taking. She knew Clearmill better than Nathan and Teresa did since she had lived in the city most of her life. "Why are you drivin' right down into the slums?" she asked, peering out the car window. "I could never live there."

"You wait till you see it, Lillie." Teresa's eyes shone.

"But I'm a high-class black, and we don't mix with slum people."

Teresa's face fell. "I guess I don't understand, Sister Lillie. I thought you would be grateful for anything. Won't you at least look at it?"

"I can't live here," Lillie declared as she looked at the rundown place. The roof was caving in and beer bottles littered the yard. Upstairs she heard raucous laughter. She closed her eyes as she remembered she had nothing else.

"We'll fix it all up," Teresa said as she watched Lillie closely.

"I will be thankful for whatever God provides for me," Lillie said automatically, but inwardly she doubted her own words.

"We will pay the rent for your home," Teresa said. "And we will get a crew together, and soon this place will be the home of your dreams."

"I will be grateful." Lillie remained stoic. During the next few weeks while the work on her place was being done, she refused to go see any progress on her new house.

Finally, Edward Jr. came home and told her, "Mama, the Mennonites have raised money for your new home, and with that money, they have remodeled the whole thing. It has new cupboards, new flooring, and new paint on the walls."

A look of disbelief covered her face. "Can you take me to see it?"

"Of course, let's go."

Lillie climbed into the car with her son. In a short time, they parked in front of the apartment house. Lillie's mouth dropped open. The house sported a new roof and new siding. Even the sidewalk in front of the house had been leveled and repaired. Lillie walked up to the kitchen door and looked inside. Teresa was putting the finishing touches on the wide white trim around the doors and windows. The whole place had received a fresh coat of paint along with new flooring. Lillie's Mennonite friends had furnished it with old Southern plantation furniture and a lovely china hutch with a set of china. *How lovely!* Lillie thought, gazing around in wonder. *But can I really make my home in the slums of the city? How can I deal with living with this kind of people?* Silently Lillie began to pray.

The next day, Edward Jr. helped her move her few possessions into her new house. She watched the upstairs neighbors as they brought their table into the yard and put their six pack of beer on it. Soon, they were laughing and making coarse jokes. Without hesitation, Lillie marched outside. "Hello, I want to tell you good black people don't live this way!"

They looked at her. "What do you mean, lady?"

Lillie put her hands on her hips. "I'm not 'lady'! You will call me Miz Lillie!"

"Yes, Miz Lillie," they chorused wide-eyed.

"We are gonna clean up this neighborhood. I will buy you a new table and a trashcan. Together we are gonna make this a place God can bless."

"Yes, Miz Lillie. We will clean it up." Immediately, they started picking up the bottles, the cans, and all the trash in the yard. Before the end of the day, their lawn looked like a new place. The trash had disappeared, and everything had been straightened up.

From that day on, the neighbors stopped having beer parties in her yard. One day Lillie climbed the flight of steps to her neighbor's apartment above her. She stopped at the top to catch her breath. *Whew! Ninety-year-old women don' have no business climbin' stairs like this. After this, they'll jes' hafta climb down 'em and come to me!* A young man answered the door. "I would like you to come and bring your friends to my house tomorrow," Lillie said.

The next day, four young people came to Lillie's front door. "Come in," she welcomed them. "I'm so glad to host my new neighbors. Now I'm slow gettin' 'round my house, can you girls help me put the food on the table?"

The two girls carried the biscuits, the pork, and the potatoes to the table. She thought about the time her mom had invited poor children to their house those many years ago.

"Now, I want to pray to God and bless this food. You all close your eyes." Lillie closed hers and began to pray, "Lawd, thank you for your provisions to us. Thank you for these dear young souls around my table. I ask you to talk to them about their souls and help me to be a vessel to bring Jesus to them. Amen, Lawd, praise de Lawd!"

"Why'd you do that, Miz Lillie?" asked the one young man.

"Because my God lives so close to me, I tell Him everything on my heart. Do you know my Lawd, young man?"

He shook his head. "He must really have gotten hold of you. You seem a little radical."

Lillie laughed. "I sure am. My Lawd has done such a miracle in my heart, I can't help being radical."

Lillie shared Jesus with them the rest of the evening. "Thank you, Miz Lillie," the young man said when he left. "We will come see you again."

"Good," Lillie said. "That would bless this ol' heart like nothin' else."

Lillie began reaching out to her neighborhood, and God blessed her efforts. She spent many hours praying for her neighbors. She looked for ways to help them when she could and took every opportunity to share her faith. Slowly, the area around her house began to change. The crime rate fell, and drinking grew less and less. Some people moved out, but better neighbors moved in.

She knew her neighbors upstairs lived in sin even though they respected her to her face. She prayed for them often. One day, she felt that she should take them a pot of soup. She cooked it and carried it upstairs to their door, her ninety-year-old joints protesting. She knocked. The door opened a crack, and one of the young women she had fed at her house recognized her. "Miz Lillie?" she asked questioningly when she saw the pot in her hand.

"Good mornin'! Praise de Lawd! The Lawd told me to bring you some soup today," Lillie said as she handed the young lady the pot.

The young woman started to weep. Lillie put her arms around her, and together they went inside. "You don' know how much we need that soup," the young woman said. "My boyfriend is out of work, I'm pregnant, and we are poor."

Lillie held the girl close and raised her hands and her voice. "Dear Jesus, look down on your chile now. Bring comfort to the heart of this here one, and please don't leave her in poverty."

The young woman wiped her eyes. "You have an amazing faith. I wish I could believe like you."

"You can," Lillie said simply. "Just trust in Jesus. Ask Him to forgive your sins and He will. It will be a journey you will never regret startin'."

The young woman shook her head sadly. "I've sinned too much. And now I'm carrying a child of a man who isn't my husband. God can never forgive all I've done."

"Oh, yes, He can," Lillie shook her finger in the girl's face and told her the brief story of her own conversion. "When He draws you to Himself, there's no gettin' 'round it. Won't you give Him your heart today?"

The young woman fell on her knees, sobs wracking her thin body. "Yes, Miz Lillie, what must I do to be saved?"

Lillie knew God had brought her to this neighborhood for this young woman. "Ask God to forgive your sins, believe in Him, and turn from your life of sin."

Lillie's heart swelled with a new love for the ones around her she had considered low-class. As the young woman prayed aloud, Lillie prayed in her heart. "Amen, hallelujah, Lawd!"

When the young woman got up from her knees, her eyes shone. "What shall I do?"

Lillie reached out and took her hand. "Ask your boyfriend if he will marry you. God can redeem any sin. This child will be a reminder of God's atonement for your sin."

"I will, Miz Lillie, and thank you for coming to see me. I am not only grateful for the food you brought, but now I'm thankin' you for bringin' me Jesus."

Lillie's heart felt light as she slowly made her way down the steps to her own home. "I don't know what He's up to, but God is workin' in that young woman's heart." She prayed for her, knowing the woman's battle had only begun.

The next day, Lillie heard a knock at her door. "Miz Lillie?" a voice asked. "Come in!" Lillie called. "I'm in my livin' room."

The young woman from upstairs walked into Lillie's home with the empty pot. "How can I ever thank you for all you've done for me?" she asked. "We are plannin' to be married next week. My baby will have a legitimate father. I'm so happy!"

"Thank you, Jesus!" Lillie cried as she pulled the young woman into her arms again. Her praise lifted her up on her toes. "And I'm gonna help you with this little one. I'm right here, and I've raised plenty of little ones. I will be a good grandma."

"Thank you again. And yes, Miz Lillie, you are like family to us already." The young woman soon left, and Lillie sat in her chair pondering the amazing love of her Father.

That afternoon the sun shone warmly, and Lillie couldn't stay inside. She delighted in the thought that another soul was beginning to experience God's sufficiency in every problem. She sat on her front porch meditating on her life and what God had done. "Lawd, the impossible has happened again. You are so good. You have humbled me by bringin' me to the slums." Her wrinkled face beamed with the joy of the Lord. "And now you have answered my prayer, and it is no longer the slums. And you've even drawn one young woman to yourself. Hallelujah!"

Lillie gazed at the tidily-kept lawns and the clean streets around her. "I never thought I'd say 'Thank ya, Lawd' for this place. You have brought me from rejection and prejudice to the cross where you have offered me pardon for my sins. You have loved me hugely. I still pray for my son, Edward Jr., and my daughter, Katherine. I will continue to believe both of them are comin' toward you. I believe they will truly repent before they die and find pardon as I have. I've done what I could in their lives. You have always been faithful to me, and I will be faithful to you until the end. Now Lawd, I'm ready to go to you when you come for those of integrity and character. My testimony is all because of you, Jesus."

Lillie leaned back and closed her eyes. Her heavenly Father, who had brought her this far in life, would continue to guide her to the end.

Endnotes

CHAPTER ONE

[1] Glenn Williams, "River of Jordan," <https://www.elyrics.net/read/r/ricky-skaggs-lyrics/river-of-jordan-lyrics.html>, accessed on April 26, 2018.

[2] Tucker Truvillion, "Tamping Ties," <https://www.allmusic.com/song/tamping-ties-mt0001391176>, accessed on April 26, 2018.

CHAPTER TWO

[1] Spiritual, "Balm in Gilead," <https://hymnary.org/text/sometimes_i_feel_discouraged_spiritual>, accessed April 26, 2018.

[2] Revelation 21:8.

[3] Negro Spiritual, "The Gospel Train," <https://en.wikipedia.org/wiki/The_Gospel_Train> accessed on April 30, 2018.

CHAPTER FOUR

[1] R. C. Ward, "Think of His Goodness to You," <https://hymnary.org/text/when_waves_of_affliction_sweep_over_the_?extended=true>, accessed on April 27, 2018.

[2] Frederick Whitfield, "Oh, How I Love Jesus," <https://hymnary.org/text/there_is_a_name_i_love_to_hear_i_love>, accessed on April 26, 2018.

CHAPTER FIVE

[1] Wallace Willis, "Swing Low, Sweet Chariot," <https://en.wikipedia.org/wiki/Swing_Low,_Sweet_Chariot>, accessed on April 30, 2018.

CHAPTER TEN

[1] "Hobo Signs," <http://www.angelfire.com/folk/famoustramp/signs.html>, accessed on July 3, 2018.

[2] Kate Hankey, "I Love to Tell the Story," 1866, <https://hymnary.org/text/i_love_to_tell_the_story_of_unseen_thing>, accessed on April 26, 2018.

CHAPTER ELEVEN

[1] Wikipedia contributors, "Chicago race riot of 1919," *Wikipedia, The Free Encyclopedia,* <https://en.wikipedia.org/w/index.php?title=Chicago_race_riot_of_1919&oldid=839048768>, accessed on April 26, 2018.

CHAPTER TWELVE

[1] History Channel, "The 1950s," 2018, A&E Television Networks, LLC , <https://www.history.com/topics/1950s>, accessed on April 27, 2018.

CHAPTER FOURTEEN

[1] 1 Corinthians 13:4–8, paraphrased.

CHAPTER FIFTEEN

[1] History Channel, "The 1950s," 2018, A&E Television Networks, LLC , <https://www.history.com/topics/1950s>, accessed on April 27, 2018.

[2] Wikipedia contributors, "Rosa Parks," *Wikipedia, The Free Encyclopedia,* <https:// . en.wikipedia.org/w/index.php?title=Rosa_Parks&oldid=837859558>, accessed on April 26, 2018.

[3] "Zipper," *How Products Are Made,* Vol. 1, <http://www.madehow.com/Volume-1/Zipper.html>, accessed on April 27, 2018.

CHAPTER SIXTEEN

[1] *West's Encyclopedia of American Law,* edition 2, S.v. "Civil Rights Movement," <http://legal-dictionary.thefreedictionary.com/civil+rights+movement>, accessed on April 27, 2018.

CHAPTER SEVENTEEN
[1] 1 Peter 3:2.

CHAPTER EIGHTEEN
[1] Acts 10.

CHAPTER TWENTY
[1] "Ruby Bridges Biography, Civil Rights Activist (1954–)," Biography, A&E Television Networks, LLC, <https://www.biography.com/people/ruby-bridges-475426>, accessed on April 27, 2018.

[2] Michele Norris, "The Woolworth Sit-In That Launched a Movement," National Public Radio, February 1, 2008, All Things Considered, <https://www.npr.org/templates/story/story.php?storyId=18615556>, accessed on April 28, 2018.

CHAPTER TWENTY-SEVEN
[1] Hebrews 3:7–8.

About the Author

Laura Smucker began to love writing when she was in fifth grade. Her creative writing teacher introduced her to various writing styles and encouraged her students to keep journals and write poetry, articles, and stories. When Laura began writing, she wrote mostly poems and sometimes stories for children. As she grew older, she realized she liked writing about real people, and she joined her first writer's email group to further develop her interest. Two of her books have been printed by Christian Aid Ministries: *Strands of Gold* and *A Reason to Hope*.

Laura grew up in Oregon but lived in Poland for ten years, where her husband, John, served as mission field director. She and John, along with four of their five children, currently live in Madras, Oregon.

A few of Laura's motivators and favorite things are coffee, chocolate, books, people, and the rich heritage of Europe.

Laura enjoys hearing from her readers and can be contacted at jolasmucker@gmail.com. You may also write to her in care of Christian Aid Ministries, P.O. Box 360, Berlin, Ohio 44610.

About Christian Aid Ministries

C hristian Aid Ministries was founded in 1981 as a nonprofit, tax-exempt 501(c)(3) organization. Its primary purpose is to provide a trustworthy and efficient channel for Amish, Mennonite, and other conservative Anabaptist groups and individuals to minister to physical and spiritual needs around the world. This is in response to the command to ". . . do good unto all men, especially unto them who are of the household of faith" (Galatians 6:10).

Each year, CAM supporters provide 15–20 million pounds of food, clothing, medicines, seeds, Bibles, Bible story books, and other Christian literature for needy people. Most of the aid goes to orphans and Christian families. Supporters' funds also help to clean up and rebuild for natural disaster victims, put up Gospel billboards in the U.S., support several church-planting efforts, operate two medical clinics, and provide resources for needy families to make their own living. CAM's main purposes for providing aid are to help and encourage God's people and bring the Gospel to a lost and dying world.

CAM has staff, warehouses, and distribution networks in Romania, Moldova, Ukraine, Haiti, Nicaragua, Liberia, Israel, and Kenya. Aside from management, supervisory personnel, and bookkeeping operations, volunteers do most of the work at CAM locations. Each year, volunteers at our warehouses, field bases, Disaster Response Services projects, and other locations donate over 200,000 hours of work.

CAM's ultimate purpose is to glorify God and help enlarge His kingdom. ". . . whatsoever ye do, do all to the glory of God" (1 Corinthians 10:31).